An Historical Outline
of
Architectural Science

ELSEVIER ARCHITECTURAL SCIENCE SERIES

Editor

HENRY J. COWAN

*The following list of subjects to be treated provides
an outline of the scope of the series*

Architecture and Climate

Designing for Health and Comfort

Thermal Performance of Buildings

Solar Control of Buildings

Principles of Air Conditioning

Vertical Transportation — Elevator and Escalator Systems
for Multi-storey Buildings

Plumbing, Sanitary Installations and Waste Disposal

Electrical Services in Buildings

Principles of Illumination and Natural Lighting

Artificial Lighting of Buildings

Architectural Acoustics

Control of Fire in Buildings

Evaluation of Building Materials

The Choice of Structure

The Design of Building Frames

Shells and Space Frames

Soil Mechanics for Architects

Models in Architecture

Computers in Architectural Design

Analytical Techniques of Planning

Architecture and Systems Analysis

An Historical Outline
of
Architectural Science

by

HENRY J. COWAN

Professor of Architectural Science
University of Sydney

ELSEVIER PUBLISHING COMPANY

AMSTERDAM – LONDON – NEW YORK

1966

ELSEVIER PUBLISHING COMPANY
335 JAN VAN GALENSTRAAT, P.O. BOX 211, AMSTERDAM

AMERICAN ELSEVIER PUBLISHING COMPANY, INC.
52 VANDERBILT AVENUE, NEW YORK, N.Y. 10017

ELSEVIER PUBLISHING COMPANY LIMITED
RIPPLESIDE COMMERCIAL ESTATE, BARKING, ESSEX

LIBRARY OF CONGRESS CATALOG CARD NUMBER 66–16716

WITH 67 ILLUSTRATIONS AND 1 TABLE

PRINTED IN THE NETHERLANDS

To Kitty

Preface

Science and engineering are traditionally taught as a logical development from experimental data, without regard to the historical sequence of the solutions or the difficulties encountered in deriving them. Architecture on the other hand, is taught largely by studying the work of great masters, and the sense of history is never absent from this treatment, even when the work is recent.

The difference reflects a wider distinction in the outlook of the scientist and the creative artist. Attempts to bridge the gap have not been lacking during the last thirty years. Many scientists have shown great interest in the history of their subject, and the discipline imposed on modern architecture by engineered structures has been explored by several eminent architects, engineers and art-historians. I have attempted to take the middle line by dealing only with those aspects of science and engineering which have influenced current architectural design, so that the historical emphasis is placed on the recent past.

This book started originally as a series of lectures delivered at the Massachusetts Institute of Technology in 1961 and at Cornell University in 1962, in each case to a mixed audience of architects and engineers. I am indebted to Professor Lawrence Anderson for the invitation to lecture at M.I.T., to Dean Burnham Kelly for the invitation to spend a semester at Cornell which afforded the leisure for editing the lectures with the help of their Rare Books Department, and to all those members of Cornell University who made my stay so pleasant and profitable.

When Sydney University instituted the Master of Building Science Degree Course for architects, engineers and building scientists in 1963, it was decided to include sixteen lectures on the history of building science, and I then expanded the material to its present form by including a survey of the scientific background to our current ideas on environmental design and on industrialized building.

While the book is primarily intended as a text for senior students, I hope that the subject will interest some general readers and in token of this expectation I have included a glossary of technical terms.

My thanks are due to Mrs. Rita Arthurson, Mrs. Marian Barber and Mrs. Nance Liddy for typing the manuscript, to Mr. Hans J. Milton, B.Arch., for preparing the drawings, and to Mr. John Dixon for the photographic work. Mr. Dixon, our Chief Laboratory Technician, also made most of the models illustrated. I am greatly indebted to all those who have previously written on the subject; their names are listed in the bibliography. Illustrations and quotations have been acknowledged where they occur. Finally I should like to express my appreciation to my colleagues, and to my past and present students for their helpful criticisms.

Sydney, December 1965. HJC

List of Contents

X   LIST OF CONTENTS

The Traditional Architectural Forms, and the Beginning of the Era of Scientific Structural Design

> Who shall doubt the secret hid
> Under Cheops' pyramid
> Was that the contractor did
> Cheops out of several millions?
> *Rudyard Kipling* [1.8]

1.1. The Two Revolutions

Structural design of a sort is almost as old as building itself. The Greeks had some quite elaborate rules for proportioning columns and lintels, and we find geometric details of buttresses and vaults in the notebooks of the Gothic masons. During the Renaissance there was a rapid multiplication of such rules, and measured drawings through the centuries have added to the number.

A feature of the empirical structural rules of classical architecture is their essentially geometric character. The strength and deformation of the structure and its general stability are considered only in a broad empirical sense. No clear distinction is made between the proportions which make an aesthetically satisfactory building and those required for a sound structure. A fortunate by-product of this emphasis on geometry rather than statics is the generally good proportioning of structurally well designed classical architecture.

One of the best-known examples is the section of Milan Cathedral in Cesariano's edition of Vitruvius' *De architectura*, published in Como in 1521, which shows the relation between the various parts in terms of equilateral triangles, circles and inscribed squares and hexagons. Although it is difficult to distinguish between the rationalization of the design, a century after the completion of the main structure, and the original intention, the triangular construction evidently gives a basis for the main proportions of the buttresses [1.1]*.

We have by no means abandoned structural design by specifying proportions. Every building by-law contains some rules for dimensioning structural members by proportions, because there is no satisfactory statical design method, and sometimes these rules are very ancient. A comparison of Alberti's *Ten Books on Architecture* [B6] ** (first printed edition 1485, M.S. ca. 1450) with many a modern building code shows up some surprising similarities.

The main weakness of empirical rules lies in their limited range of applicability, and in the difficulty of distinguishing between those based on sound empiricism from others derived from old superstitions or from mistaken generalizations of features found in famous buildings. Although proportional rules are no longer used as the main basis for determining structural dimensions, few architects or engineers fail to inform themselves about previous work before embarking on the design of an unconventional structure.

The chief difficulty in a procedure based entirely on development from precedent is the verification of the new design. The pace of innovation is today too fast to make gradual adaptation from previous structures feasible. The public reacts more unfavourably than formerly to collapse or serious structural damage when the shuttering is struck. We can no longer afford to build a substantial prototype structure, as was frequently done in previous centuries, to test the design.

The ever-increasing trend towards structural design based on extensive numerical calculations has been mainly responsible for the growth of structural engineering as a separate profession, whose practitioners have a basically different educational background from that of architects.

In the late nineteenth century the prevailing philosophy of architectural design tended to accentuate the differences in outlook

---

* Numbers in brackets refer to the References, pp. 165—170.
** Refers to the Bibliography, pp. 158—164.

between architectural and structural design which the intellectually differing problems of the two aspects encouraged. If it was possible to place any desired form of ornamentation on any economically appropriate structure, it was unnecessary to consider both aspects together.

The revolution in architectural thought during the twentieth century has entirely altered this relationship. Only in comparatively simple or conventional buildings is it possible at the present time to consider the over-all architectural concept without reference to the structure.

The change has been largely caused, and certainly strongly encouraged, by economic circumstances. Greatly improved living standards have increased the cost of labour to such an extent that many traditional methods of construction have completely vanished and been replaced by processes more amenable to mechanization. The virtual disappearance of elaborately carved natural stone as a structural material is aesthetically a great loss, but it was inevitable if one bears in mind that the mason had to form the shape by cutting small chips slowly from the solid block.

The replacement of natural stone and brick, laid in mortar, by steel and reinforced concrete basically altered structural mechanics. Emphasis shifted from determining the conditions of equilibrium of loosely joined masses of material to checking the stresses within the material. The revolution in structural design was therefore twofold. On the one hand the development of mechanics made it possible to place design on a more rational basis, on the other hand the introduction of the new manufactured materials made a more scientific approach essential.

1.2. Structure in the Ancient World

Only two major structural materials were available to the Ancient World, viz. timber and natural or artificial stone. Timber has moderate strength in both tension and compression, but limited durability, and hardly any ancient and medieval timber structures have survived to the present day. Natural stone, concrete and brick have generally good durability and high compressive strength, but their resistance to tension is poor. These deficiencies were largely responsible for the limitations of permanent structures prior to the eighteenth century.

The simplest form of structure consists of a combination of beams and columns. The horizontal members are subject to bending which induces tensile stresses on the lower face, and this severely limits the span of un-reinforced masonry structures, however carefully designed. In most Egyptian temples there is little evidence of structural design, e.g. in the huge Temple at Edfou the depth of the lintels is actually greater than their span [B2]. In Greek architecture the stone is utilized a little more economically than in Egypt, but the structural limitations of stone lintels are immediately apparent when one examines, for example, the closely spaced columns of the Temple of Diana of Ephesus, built by Dinocrates ca. 330 B.C. [B2]. It was perhaps justly regarded as one of the Seven Wonders of the World; but as an example of structural engineering it is undistinguished.

All the great masonry spans prior to the invention of reinforcement in the nineteenth century were therefore bridged by means of vaulting. It seems likely that the arch developed from the use of corbels, i.e. stones cantilevered from the wall into the opening so that successive layers reduced the span. This form of construction was employed more than three thousand years ago, e.g. in the sub-terranean Treasury of Atreus at Mycenae, ca. 1185 B.C. The corbels are subject to tension on the upper face, but the span of the opening is reduced progressively by layers of stones or bricks, each layer cantilevering from the previous layer by only a short distance so that the tensile stresses are quite low.

The stress-distribution can be transformed by the addition of a keystone, which presumably accounts for the great attention paid to decoration of this stone and the ceremonial which commonly accompanied its installation. While the keystone is no different from any other member of the arch, the closing of the ribs places the stone entirely in compression, provided the shape of the arch and the direction of the joints is suitable.

Since the compressive strength of stone, brick and concrete is about ten times its tensile strength, the potential maximum span is increased accordingly. Some of the Roman vaults were of tremendous size. The dome of the Pantheon (Fig. 1.1) has a diameter of 142 ft. which was not equalled again until the 19th century.

Roman arches and domes were almost invariably circular. This may have been a matter of convenience in setting out the work; but it is more likely that the circle was used because it was regarded as the most perfect curve.*

In view of the ingenuity of their construction methods it is surprising that the Romans paid little attention to the mechanically most suitable shape, the catenary arch, or to the potentialities of buttresses. In consequence, the walls of the Pantheon are 20 ft. thick, and although relieving arches are used, the use of material is extravagant.

Roman concrete and mortar was of very high quality (*see* Section 2.6). Natural cement of volcanic origin was used for the best work, but even the lime mortar, probably because of the admixture of brick dust, was remarkably strong [1.3]. Neither the Greek nor the Gothic builders achieved a comparable strength in their mortar joints.

The quality of the materials used in Mesopotamia was much inferior, and this probably accounts for the discovery of the catenary arch, which alone is subject to pure compression under its own weight. For example, the Great Arch of the Palace of Ctesiphon built in 550 A.D. with mud bricks, lightly burnt, and set in clay mortar, has a span of 90 ft. and a height of 112 ft. [B16]. Its survival for 14 centuries, mostly without care or protection, is remarkable.

---

* Even though structural evidence was to the contrary, this view was reiterated, on geometric or religious grounds, up to the late nineteenth century: –

"Many architects, especially the worst, have been very curious in designing out-of-the-way arches—elliptical arches, and four-centred arches, so called, and other singularities. The good architects have been generally content, and we for the present will be so, with God's arch, the arch of the rainbow and of the apparent Heaven, and which the sun shapes for us as it sets and rises." (John Ruskin, *Stones of Venice*, 1853, [1.2].)

The catenary dome survives to the present day in the mud huts of central Africa.

Fig. 1.1.   The interior of the Pantheon in Rome, built in 123 *A.D.*, in the reign of the Emperor Hadrian. The building is still in use today as a church. (From *The Architecture of A. Palladio*, published from the Manuscript in Worcester College, Oxford (London, 1742).)

1.3. Gothic Structure

After the fall of the Roman Empire no significant structural advance took place for several centuries. The civilized world was split up into a large number of units, so that resources for building on the Roman scale were no longer available, and much of the Roman technical knowledge was lost. The achievements of the Gothic master masons are the more remarkable: they demonstrate that intricate structural solutions can be created without a knowledge of the basic mechanical theory. A great effort was devoted to the building of the cathedrals: –

"In that year (1144), for the first time, the faithful of Chartres could be seen hauling the carts which were loaded with stone, timber, corn or anything else needed for the work on the cathedral. As if touched by a magic wand, the turrets rose to the sky . . . Men and women were seen dragging heavy loads through the marshes and chanting the praise of God's works." (From the Chronicle of Robert of Mont-Saint-Michel, as quoted by Dehio in *Die Kirchliche Baukunst des Abendlandes*, Stuttgart, 1892–1901, Vol. II, p. 22.)

The other important factor was the careful study of precedent. The most daring features developed gradually over a period of almost three centuries. Spans varied but little and only twice exceeded 50 ft. Even so the chronicles suggest that there were many failures.

The daring of Gothic construction is best illustrated by its simpler structural features which are readily checked; e.g. the single interior column in the Chapel of the Nine Altars, at Fountains Abbey in Yorkshire has a slenderness ratio of 70. No current building regulation would permit this, yet it has survived for centuries with inadequate lateral stiffening.

It has frequently been claimed that the Gothic master masons must have had a knowledge of the principles of mechanics to achieve such marvellous economy in the use of material and precision in the alignment of their flying buttresses; but it is certain that no modern mechanical concepts were used. According to the medieval mind, a stone dropped when released from a height, not because it was acted on by a force, but because being of the earth it returned to it. Since the essential similarity between the vertical forces due to the weight of the structure and the horizontal thrusts at the supports was not clearly understood, no useful solutions could be formulated.

Some of the notebooks of the Gothic master builders have been preserved. They show that geometry was extensively used in the design of the cathedrals (Fig. 1.2). However, geometric constructions which might help to establish lines of force date only from the

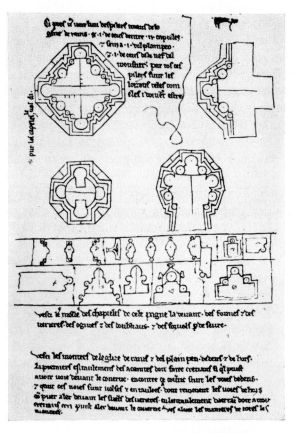

Fig. 1.2. Notes on geometry from the notebooks of Villard de Honnecourt, ca. 1235, now in the Bibliothèque Nationale, Paris.

Fig. 1.3. Section through the Choir of Ely Cathedral. The original buttresses are shown in the south *(right)* face, whereas the buttresses on the north *(left)* face were constructed a century later. The earlier design is geometrically simpler, but the greater structural efficiency of the later design is evident. (From D. H. S. Cranage, *Cathedrals and How They were Built*, (London, 1951).)

late 15th century, and are probably rationalizations of Gothic structural ideas made in the light of the new knowledge of the Renaissance.

The development of the correct form by trial and error can sometimes be traced, as for example in the flying buttresses of the Choir of Ely Cathedral (Fig. 1.3). Occasionally structural weaknesses resulted in interesting new features, e.g. the inverted arches of Wells Cathedral were added a century and a half after the erection of the main structure [B2]. Since the vault over the crossing is much higher than over the nave or the transept, the lateral thrust of the ribs sets up a bending moment in the pillars supporting the tower, and the inverted arches were introduced to transmit the inward component of the thrust from the lower vaults to the ground.

The ingenuity of the Gothic master masons in creating beauty out of structural necessity stands unsurpassed. Architects of succeeding generations frequently preferred to hide their structure behind screen walls and false ceilings, and the Gothic Revival aimed at least partly at reviving the use of structural form as a means of architectural expression. On this ground the revival was bound to fail. When Ruskin published the last volume of *The Stones of Venice* in 1853 [1.2], iron was already well established, and three years later Bessemer's invention of an economical process for the manufacture of steel rendered obsolete a form of construction based on the principle of balancing masses of stone joined only be a weak mortar. Within fifty years it became possible to build structures with the same over-all dimensions as the largest Gothic cathedrals at a small fraction of the cost by using steel or reinforced concrete.

The difference between Gothic structure and between steel or reinforced concrete construction is most clearly demonstrated by the theory of the buttress, even though this theory was unknown in the Middle Ages, and the buttress was employed with understanding of the principles involved only in Neo-Gothic architecture (Fig. 1.4).

Since buttresses are built up from stone blocks joined by a relatively weak mortar, it is necessary to shape them so as to avoid tension across the joints, i.e. by ensuring that the point of action of the resultant falls within the middle third of the cross-section (Fig. 1.5).

In order to eliminate tension across the mortar joints it is therefore necessary to widen the buttress so as to keep the resultant of the inclined reaction (due to the flying buttress or the wall of the aisle) and of the vertical reaction (due to the overlying mass of stonework) within the middle third at any horizontal section. The

Fig. 1.4. The middle-third rule—when a load is placed outside the middle third, tension develops on the opposite side, and the joint opens up. (Architectural Science Laboratory, University of Sydney.)

pinnacles, which form a prominent feature of the elevation, fulfil an important structural function in deflecting the lateral thrust of the flying buttresses downwards, and the width of the buttress is thereby reduced. The principle of adding dead weight to deflect the line of thrust naturally increases the quantity of material. Although a few cases of overstressing may have occurred when very soft stone was used, the strength of the material is not normally critical in Gothic construction. In modern structures weak joints can be eliminated, and the amount of material reduced until the maximum permissible stresses are reached. This change in technique is

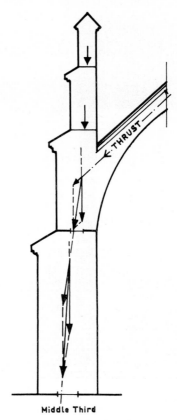

Fig. 1.5. The theory of the buttress, based on keeping the resultant force within the middle third.

responsible for the relative lightness of modern structures, which may weigh less than one per cent of a similar traditional example.

1.4. The Renaissance and the Beginnings of the Study of Mechanics

The fifteenth century brought a revival of classical ideas in architecture and in science. The beginnings of structural mechanics can be traced back to Ancient Greece. Archimedes discovered the principle of the lever, and was able to determine the centre of gravity of simple geometric figures. Most of the significant practical applications were, however, in the field of military engineering which was then, as it is today, given particular attention. The simple machines employed by the Greeks and the Romans in the transport and erection of heavy blocks of stone were mainly by-products of military equipment.

The failure of the Greek philosophers to put their considerable scientific knowledge to more practical use was to a large extent due to a reluctance to consider the strength of a building as being worthy of scientific study. Their most elaborate mechanisms, apparently deliberately, served no significant engineering purpose (Fig. 1.6).

While the Greeks bequeathed to architecture a marvellously complete system of geometry, the serious study of structural mechanics commenced only with the Renaissance. The first preoccupation was, as in Roman times, with the handling of great weights (Fig. 1.7).

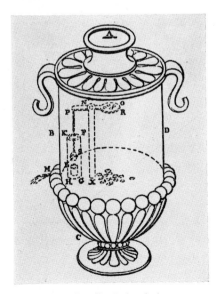

Fig. 1.6. Automatic machine for dispensing holy water, operated by a coin placed in a slot, invented by Hero of Alexandria, perhaps as early as 100 *B.C.*

Fig. 1.7.   Hoisting tackle. (From the Leoni edition of Alberti's *Ten Books of Architecture* [B6].)

Before any progress could be made towards an analysis of the forces acting on a structure, it was necessary to define the notion of force as a vectorial unit, i.e. as a quantity having both magnitude and direction. This was a task which called for a considerable effort of abstraction. Leonardo da Vinci was the first to solve this problem [1.4]. He considered the condition of equilibrium of two inclined strings carrying a weight; by drawing to scale the forces in the strings and the forces due to the weight in the direction in which they were acting he obtained the parallelogram of forces, which is the key to most problems of elementary structural mechanics (Fig. 1.8).

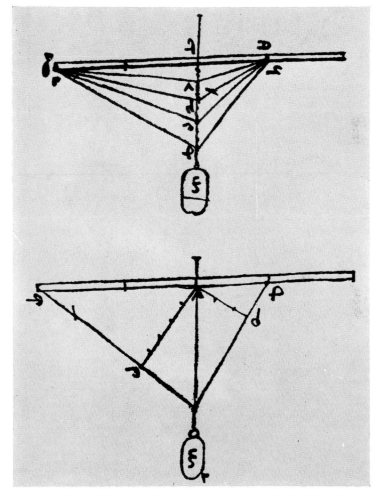

Fig. 1.8. The parallelogram of forces. (From Leonardo da Vinci's notebooks; Arundel MSS, begun in 1508, now in the British Museum.)

Leonardo's work had no immediate effect on design. Although the architects of the Renaissance revived the Roman methods, they made few advances. Applications of mechanics during the next two centuries concentrated on the handling of heavy weights.

The best-known operation of this kind was the erection of the obelisk on the piazza in front of St. Peter's by Domenico Fontana in 1586 (Fig. 1.9). Even this is dwarfed by the earlier Roman effort in bringing the same obelisk from Egypt. The operation throws some light on contemporary labour conditions. A large number of people were needed to operate the hoisting gear. Fontana reports that the most stringent disciplinary measures, including the death penalty, were decreed and a public executioner was ready on the building site; yet the late sixteenth century was a relatively enlightened age, and the Pope one of its more humane princes.

Fontana was later the joint architect for the erection of the dome of St. Peter's in accordance with Michelangelo's design, and it seems unlikely that mechanical theory played any direct part in that operation.

Indirectly, however, the growth of new knowledge made itself felt in structural design. The Renaissance developed a highly elaborate system of proportions for the design of both the plan and the elevation of buildings (Fig. 1.10), and in some instances this clearly helped towards a correct resolution of the thrust. The proportions for the classical orders were laid down in minute detail by Alberti, ca. 1450, and in the later editions of Vitruvius.

Although there are only five architectural *incunabula*, all in Latin (three editions of Vitruvius, and one each of Alberti and Gripaldi), there were several dozen architectural books available

---

Fig. 1.9. Erection of the obelisk on the piazza in front of St. Peter's, Rome. (From *Della trasportatione dell' obelisco Vaticano etc.* by Domenico Fontana (Rome 1590).)
Fontana's detailed account of the operation is interesting because it shows how small a part theory played in the building operations of the time. Two pages of his book are devoted to a calculation of the volume, and hence the weight of the obelisk; but the alignment of the ropes was determined with the help of a miniature lifting tower hoisting a lead obelisk.

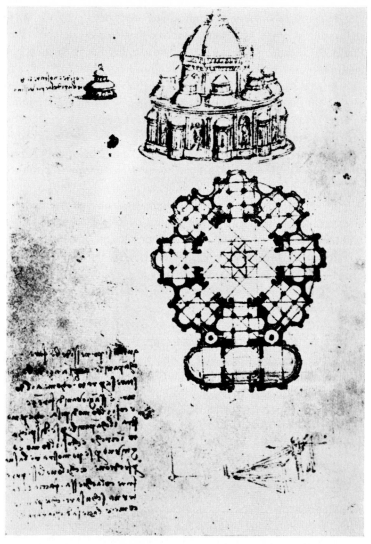

Fig. 1.10. Design for a church, based on the proportional relation $\theta = 1 + \sqrt{2}$. (From Leonardo da Vinci's Notebooks; Bibliothèque Nationale, Paris, MS 2037.)

in five languages by the middle of the sixteenth century. Proportions were not confined to visual aspects. Alberti specified the shape and thickness of arches, and even the proportions of invisible structural members such as piers, piles and pile caps. The advent of printing facilitated the interchange of numerical data on structural proportions; Renaissance structure became considerably lighter and more elegant than that of the Romans, even though the proportions had no strictly scientific basis.

The scientific knowledge of many of the Renaissance architects must also have helped them towards a better understanding of structural behaviour. While Christopher Wren, a professor of astronomy before he turned to architecture, apparently used no theoretical mechanics in his design of St. Paul's, his appreciation of the structural problem is evident in the design of the dome (Fig. 1.11).

The first, if somewhat oversimplified solution of the masonry arch, dates from the same time. In 1695 De La Hire, in his *Traité de Méchanique*, argued that the shape of the arch must be such that for each block the resultant of its own weight and of the pressure of the preceding block is perpendicular to the face of the next block (Fig. 1.12).

The arch is then stable even if there is no friction between the joints. The thesis of the absence of friction can be demonstrated most clearly if the wedge-shaped blocks of stone are replaced by circular spheres which can roll over each other (Fig. 1.13a). This argument is of some interest in the history of architectural science, because it is probably the first result of structural mechanics which was applied to a practical problem. The dome of St. Peter's showed signs of cracking in the middle of the 18th century, 150 years after its construction. Among the experts consulted was Giovanni Poleni, then Professor of Experimental Philosophy at the University of Padua. He solved the problem by assembling a number of spheres, each proportional to the weight of the corresponding blocks of stone, on a string and then determining experimentally the shape of the catenary (Fig. 1.13b).

In 1732 Danizy had already observed from model experiments

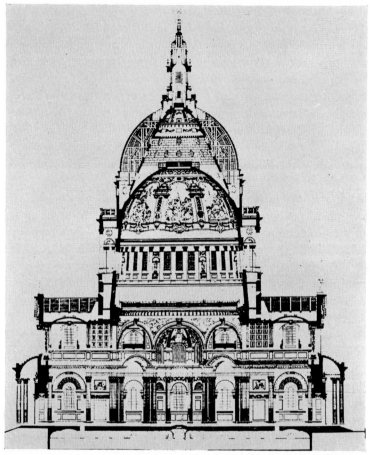

Fig. 1.11. Cross section of St. Paul's Cathedral looking east. The brick structure between the inner and outer dome (built ca. 1698), is corbelled, like the Treasury of Atreus, and it supports the timber framework of the outer dome and the stone lantern. The cone has been criticized as structurally dishonest, but given the principal dimensions of height and span, the shape conforming to the line of thrust is visually unacceptable. (From a drawing by Arthur F. E. Poley, *Sir Christopher Wren*, by John Summerson (London, 1953).)

at the Academy of Montpellier that failure of an arch commonly occurred by rotation of the voussoirs (Fig. 1.14). This was the basis of the solution presented by Coulomb in 1773 [1.5]. However, as Coulomb confined himself to determining the limits of the thrust necessary for stability and did not give definite rules for the design of arches, the value of his work was not appreciated until the 19th century, when mechanics finally became the basis of the design of masonry arches. By then it was already on the verge of obsolescence as a form of construction.

Indeed, it is doubtful if the design of masonry domes was ever properly based on mechanics. Sir Edmund Beckett, who was reputed to be an authority on the subject following the presentation of a paper in the Memoirs of the Royal Institute of British Architects in 1871, claimed in an article in Volume 7 of the Ninth Edition of the Encyclopaedia Britannica, published in 1877, that a hemisphere of stone or brick needs to have a ratio of thickness/diameter of 0.023 for stability. Only one noteworthy dome is thinner; this is the inner dome of St. Paul's, which is built of 18 in. brickwork, whereas 0.023 diameters would require 28 in. The main structural

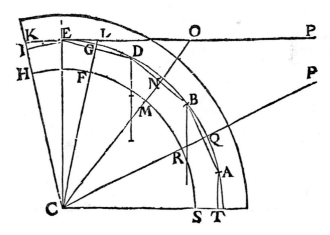

Fig. 1.12. De La Hire's solution of the masonry arch. (From *Traité de Méca-nique* (Paris, 1729).)

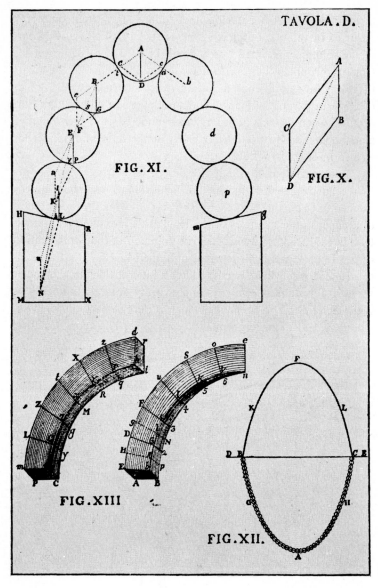

TAVOLA . D.

FIG. XI.

FIG. X.

FIG. XIII

FIG. XII.

(a)

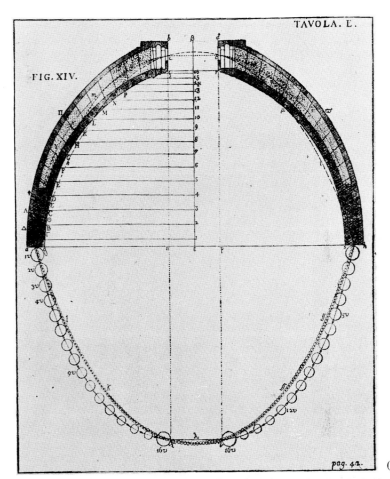

Fig. 1.13. Poleni's use of the catenary for the solution of the masonry arch and his solution of the correct line of thrust for the Dome of St. Peter's. (From *Memorie istoriche della Gran Cupola del Tempio Vaticano* (Padua, 1748).)

feature of the roof, however, is the brick cone which merges with the inner dome near the supports (*see* Fig. 1.11). Beckett appreciated that hoop tension develops in a spherical dome if the angle subtended at the centre exceeds 52°, and suggested hoop reinforcement in the lower courses of the brickwork.

Fig. 1.14. A lead model shows the failure of a voussoir arch by the formation of four hinges. Three hinges make the rigid arch statically determinate, four turn it into a mechanism. (Architectural Science Laboratory, University of Sydney.)

There are basically two problems in the stability of the spherical dome of masonry or plain concrete. One is the development of hoop tension in domes with a high ratio of rise to span. The remedy is to use a shallow dome, and this form of construction survives to this day in Spain, where shallow brick domes are still being built.

This solution, however, produces a large horizontal reaction which has to be accommodated (Fig. 1.15); only in a dome with vertical springings is this reaction absorbed by the hoop tension. The problem of transmitting the horizontal reaction of a dome with inclined springings to the foundations is considerable in a high masonry building, and it requires either very thick walls or an elaborate system of buttresses.

The problem is further complicated by the great weight of a large masonry dome. A hemisphere of stone, 100 ft. diameter and 1 ft. thick, weighs approximately 1,000 tons. The dome of St. Peter's, Rome, weighs approximately 10,000 tons.

Since the development of modern materials both problems have been solved, and we can today build a relatively shallow dome of substantial span at a great height above the foundations (*see* Table 4.1). While the most obvious difference between the classical and the modern dome is in the ratio of rise to span, this is due to different artistic and functional concepts, rather than to mechanical causes.

1.5. The Age of Reason and the Foundations of Classical Structural Mechanics

The failure to derive a useful theory of structural mechanics prior to the 19th century was due largely to the complexity of the

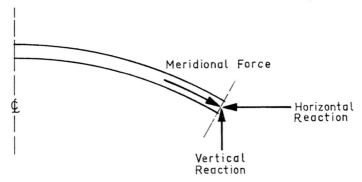

Fig. 1.15. Only a dome with vertical springings, e.g. a hemispherical dome, has vertical reactions. A shallow spherical dome requires horizontal reactions.

architectural structures of the time; indeed many of the large buildings of the Renaissance and the Baroque period defy theoretical analysis to the present day.

Even with simpler structures, however, like the timber trusses of Palladio (*see* Section 3.1), scientific design depended on the formation of a limiting criterion, since no solution for relating the loads acting on the structure to the forces in it can be applied unless the physical properties of the building materials are known.

Experimental determination of the physical properties of the materials can be traced with certainty to the early Renaissance, and some tests were probably carried out earlier. Leonardo da Vinci described in his Notebooks a machine for testing the tensile strength of a wire [1.6]: –

"The object of this test is to find the load an iron wire can carry. Attach an iron wire 2 braccia long to something that will firmly support it, then attach a basket or any similar container to the wire and feed into the basket some fine sand through a small hole placed in the end of a hopper. A spring is fixed so that it will close the hole as soon as the wire breaks. The basket is not upset while falling, since it falls through a very short distance. The weight of the sand and the location of the fracture of the wire are to be recorded. The test is to be repeated several times to check the results."

The machine is remarkably similar to one still in use today for testing cement briquettes.

The relative lack of progress in determining the physical properties of materials during the next two centuries was due mainly to attempts to test full-size pieces of material with dead weights, which proved very expensive and sometimes impossible. With the development of the lever testing machine in the 18th century systematic testing became practicable, and in 1751 Petrus van Musschenbroek, Professor of Physics at the University of Leyden in Holland, published in his book *Essai de Physique* the first extensive data on the strength of materials.

The elastic nature of building materials was first discovered by Robert Hooke, who presented his findings in one of the Cutlerian lectures to the Royal Society of London in 1678 [1.7]: –

"Take a wire 20 or 30 or 40 feet long, and fasten the upper part thereof to a nail, and to the other end fasten a scale to receive the weights. Then with a pair of compasses take the distance of the bottom of the scale from the ground or floor underneath, and set down the said distance, then put in weights into the said scale and measure the several stretchings of the said string, and set them down. Then compare the several stretchings of the said string, and you will find that they always bear the same proportions one to the other that the weights do that made them."

From this Hooke concluded: –

"It is very evident that the Rule or Law of Nature in every springing body is that the force or power thereof to restore itself to its natural position is always proportionate to the distance or space it is removed therefrom, whether it be by a rarefaction, or the separation of its parts the one from the other, or by a condensation, or crowding of those parts nearer together. Nor is it observable in these bodies only, but in all other springy bodies whatsoever, whether metal, wood, stones, baked earth, hair, horns, silk, bones, sinews, glass and the like."

In brief, the deformation of an elastic body is directly proportional to the applied force. Hooke's Law ceases to apply at high loads when materials begin to suffer permanent structural damage, and in consequence it cannot be used as a basis for determining the failing loads. Since measurements of elastic deformation were possible only in very simple cases before the 19th century, the early elastic theories were generally checked by tests to destruction. Elastic behaviour and failure, however, are concerned with essentially different properties of the same material, and the resulting discrepancies in the experiments caused much confusion in the 17th and 18th centuries.

It was only during the 19th century that the perfection of extensometers for measuring small strains put the elastic theory on a sound experimental basis, and the verification by tests to destruction ceased to be necessary. Hooke's Law became the basis of an elaborate and highly mathematical theory of elasticity which could be used with confidence without constant resort to experiment.

In recent years, however, we have developed qualms about the soundness of elasticity as the main basis of structural design, and have recognized in the confusion of the pioneers of the Age of Reason a basic structural problem which requires further consideration.

Chapter 2

One-dimensional Structures, and the Invention of Steel and Reinforced Concrete Construction

> "If Mr. Ruskin be right", wrote the reviewer soon after the publication of *the Stones of Venice* in 1853, "all architects, and all the architectural teaching of the last three hundred years, must have been wrong."
> "That is indeed precisely the fact", replied Ruskin in a later edition, "and the very thing I meant to say, which indeed I thought I had said over and over again. I believe the architects of the last three centuries to have been wrong; wrong without exception; wrong totally, and from the foundation. This is exactly the point I have been trying to prove, from the beginning of this work to the end of it."
> *Introduction to* The Stones of Venice [1.2]

2.1. The Beginnings of Modern Structural Engineering

The emergence of structural engineering depended on the development of a simple and accurate theory of design, and on the mass production of materials with the requisite properties; both were needed before any real progress could be made.

While structural mechanics had been seriously studied since the 15th century, the most significant developments occurred in France after the foundation of the *École des Ponts et Chaussées*. Following the Revolution the schools and universities of the Old Regime were discontinued, and the *École Polytechnique*, founded in 1795, became the main centre of theoretical mechanics.

Somewhat surprisingly, one of the most difficult problems, the buckling of columns, was solved by Euler as early as 1757. Study of the theory of bending, commenced by Galileo ca. 1600, extended over two centuries. The analysis of the truss, generally regarded as one of the simplest problems in modern structural mechanics, received no serious consideration until the middle of the 19th century.

In the 18th century cast iron and wrought iron were being produced in England on a commercial scale. For the first time a durable material of high tensile strength became available in large quantities for use in building. The new materials, moreover, could be shaped with considerable ease during manufacture, and possessed the ideal elastic properties assumed in the theory.

The first major iron structure, a cast iron arch bridge, was built over the Severn at Coalbrookdale in England, in 1779 by Abraham Darby [B 17]. This bridge has a span of 100 ft. 6 in., and is still in use today. Its construction was preceded by lengthy deliberations during which designs in masonry were at first favoured. The design eventually adopted is reminiscent of a stone arch, in which the mortar joints are replaced by the iron ribs, and the blocks of masonry become voids. The connections of the iron elements are based on standard timber joints. A more logical use of iron only developed at the turn of the century, when the material was increasingly used in bridge construction and later in buildings.

The possession of the right material proved at first more important than theoretical knowledge, and most of the early development of building in iron and steel took place in England. During much of this time England and France were at war, which discouraged intellectual contact and caused ideas originating on the other side of the English Channel to be treated with some disdain. In consequence, British engineers of the later 18th and early 19th centuries were fifty years behind the French school in their theoretical work, and relied largely on load tests for the verification of their designs. English structural engineering books during the early 19th century place strong emphasis on practical experience, and sometimes refer to the use of advanced theoretical methods in slighting terms. The discrepancy between French theory and English practical experience is noted on a number of occasions; usually it is the result of attempts to use an elastic theory for verifying results obtained from tests to destruction.

2.2. Early Structures in Iron and Steel

The advent of iron resulted in a return to the earliest and simplest form of structure, the beam supported by columns.

Whereas the stone lintels of Greek and Renaissance architecture rarely spanned more than a few feet, iron beams were capable of spanning the nave of any medieval cathedral. Being simply supported, they could do so, moreover, without exerting a large lateral thrust.

The use of the new material was confined mainly to the industrial buildings, which began to make their appearance in the late 18th century. The designers of industrial buildings usually did not engage in work of a more conventionally architectural character, and two separate professions began to emerge. The Institution of Civil Engineers was founded in 1818, and the Royal Institute of British Architects in 1834.

The economic basis for the large-scale use of iron was, in the first instance, the need for fireproof construction in warehouses containing combustible materials, which became an important consideration with the growth of the factories (*see also* Section 5.6). Later a number of disastrous fires in multi-storey factories roused public opinion to the introduction of building regulations requiring fire-resistant construction for public buildings generally.*

A typical floor of an English fireproof industrial building at the beginning of the 19th century was carried by cast iron girders supported on solid walls or cast iron columns, the floor consisted of brick jack arches spanning between the girders, with the spandrels filled with rubble or weak concrete (Fig. 2.1). For large spans the weight of the girder was reduced by cutting holes in the web, but the shape of the openings was determined by considerations of

---

* This problem, tackled so energetically in the 19th century, was age-old. Alberti writes [B6, p. 150]: –

"I am entirely for having the roofs of temples arched, as well because it gives them greater dignity, as because it makes them more durable. And indeed I know not how it happens that we shall hardly meet any one temple whatsoever that has not fallen into the calamity of fire . . . Ceasar owned that Alexandria escaped being burnt, when he himself took it, because its roofs were vaulted".

While the timber roof alone was not fireproof, the Gothic vaults still required a timber roof over the stonework as weather protection, an arrangement which was hardly functional or economical.

If one bears in mind that the weight of masonry vaults increases rapidly with the span, the arguments in favour of the use of iron for public buildings were very strong.

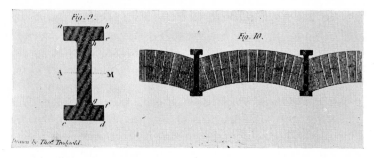

Fig. 2.1. Cast iron beams and brick jack arches (from Tredgold, (1824), [B22]).

appearance and of convenience during casting and subsequent handling.

Occasionally the holes were arranged so as to imitate a timber truss, with diagonals and verticals. This type of girder was frequently castigated in the early 20th century as an illogical imitation of timber, which undoubtedly provided the inspiration. The form is, however, quite appropriate to a cast material, and it is interesting to find its reappearance in recent years in precast concrete construction.

The architectural use of cast iron was mainly limited to ornamental work. The elaborate, and sometimes beautiful, balcony screens of old houses in New Orleans and in Sydney, are typical examples. There were only a few architects in the first half of the century, such as John Nash, who used cast iron as a structural material, e.g., in the 1821 additions to Buckingham Palace, and more extensively in the Royal Pavilion in Brighton, where the unusually tall and slender columns in the kitchen are shaped as palm trees [B17]. Cast iron columns in public buildings were generally ornate, and frequently imitated classical forms.

The columns were notably more successful than the cast iron beams, partly because the material due to its high compressive strength is more suitable for columns, and partly because the ease with which it could be decorated commended it to the Victorian age. Columns modelled on one of the classical orders were soon used in industrial buildings, and the manufacture of cast iron columns in Britain ceased only during the First World War, when the facilities were required for armament production; cast iron beams became obsolete well before the end of the century.

In 1847 Henry Fielder obtained a patent for making compound beams by rivetting together cast and wrought iron sections, plates and angles. Wrought iron cost twice the price of cast iron, but it was twice as strong in tension, more consistent in its properties and less susceptible to damage by shock. In 1856 Henry Bessemer invented the process named after him for blowing air through the fluid pig iron, instead of reducing the carbon content by the traditional laborious puddling process. In 1885 Dorman Long and Co. commenced to roll steel joists, and both cast iron and wrought iron beams soon became uneconomical.

In 1883 Sir Benjamin Baker commenced the construction of the Firth-of-Forth Bridge near Edinburgh, whose clear span of 1,710 ft. established steel as the ideal material for longspan structures. In the same year William Le Baron Jenney used it in the first skeleton steel frame, in the Home Insurance Building in Chicago [B24]. By the turn of the century steel had become accepted as the principal material for large-scale construction.

2.3. The Theory of Bending

While virtually all the initial practical development leading up to the modern steel frame took place in the English-speaking countries in little more than a century, the theory of bending was being perfected in France.

Since the bending problem is of such fundamental importance, it is not surprising to find reference to it in Leonardo da Vinci's Notebooks. Galileo, however, gave the first solution. With reference to Figs. 2.2 and 2.3, he stated [2.1]: –

"It is clear that, if the cylinder breaks, fracture will occur at the point B where the edge of the mortice acts as a fulcrum for the lever BC, to which the force is applied; the thickness of the solid BA is the other arm of the lever along which is located the resistance. The resistance opposes the separation of the part BD lying outside

Fig. 2.2. Illustration of the bending test. (From Galileo Galilei, *Discorsi e dimostrazioni matematiche interno a due nuove scienze*, Elzevir, Leyden (Holland) 1638.)

the wall, from the portion lying inside. From the preceding it follows that the magnitude of the force applied at C bears to the magnitude of the resistance the same ratio, which half the length BA bears to the length BC."

Thus Galileo found correctly that the resistance is proportional to the first power of the width and the second power of the depth,

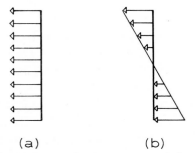

(a)   (b)

Fig. 2.3. Stress distribution implied by Galileo's solution (a), and true stress distribution (b).

and inversely proportional to the distance of the load from the support. However, his answer is three times the true value. Galileo presumably observed an initial tension failure at A, and consequently decided that there was a tensile force acting between the support and the cantilever. By limiting his argument to forces he tacitly assumed uniform stress distribution. We now know that the stress varies from a maximum compressive stress to a maximum tensile stress; but before a variable stress-distribution could be conceived it was necessary to consider the deformation of the beam.

Robert Hooke in 1678 described his experiments on springs and wires (*see* Section 1.5), in which he showed that most building materials behaved elastically under load and that deformation was proportional to the load. He also observed that the fibres on the convex side of a beam are extended, and the fibres on the concave side are compressed. In 1705 Jacob Bernoulli published a dissertation on the deflection of beams, in which he assumed that vertical sections which are plane before bending remain plane after bending. Although it was difficult to prove at the time, this assumption is now easily demonstrated with a flexible beam, e.g. one made from rubber, or confirmed by strain measurements. All the basic propositions had now been enunciated, but the correct solution was only obtained in 1773 by C. A. Coulomb [1.5]. Even then it received little attention until L. M. H. Navier gave a more direct proof in 1826.

The publication of Navier's lectures under the title *Résumé des leçons données à l'Ecole des Ponts et Chaussées sur l'application de la mécanique à l'établissement des constructions et des machines* was an event of great importance, because it was the first text-book on the theory of structures and the strength of materials [B16]. For the first time the various solutions were brought together and integrated. Navier's presentation was so successful that there are books still in print today which closely follow his method.

Navier's bending theory considers an originally straight beam bent into a circular arc by a bending moment. Since it is assumed that plane sections remain plane after bending, all originally straight vertical lines converge on a centre of curvature. The top fibres consequently become longer, i.e. they are strained in tension, and the bottom fibres become shorter, i.e. they are strained in compression. At the neutral axis the tension changes into compression, and in a symmetrical beam the neutral axis is evidently at half-depth. The strain, which is defined as the change in length over the original length, can now be derived from the geometry of the deformed beam. The stresses, which are the forces acting on infinitely small individual fibres, are then obtained from Hooke's Law. The moment of resistance of the beam consists of the sum of the moments of the forces in the individual fibres about the neutral axis, and this must, for equilibrium, equal the moment acting on the section. On combining these three steps, we obtain the required relation between the bending moment and the maximum stress produced in the section.

2.4. Conventional Design of Steel Frames

This equation has remained the accepted basis for the design of beams. Navier was emphatic in his book that we must know the limit up to which structures behave perfectly elastically and suffer no permanent deformation. The maximum permissible stress is then related to this limit by the factor of safety, which has been progressively reduced with better control over loads, materials, construction and methods of analysis; for steel structures it is now about $1\frac{2}{3}$. Navier rejected the 18th century attempts to find ultimate strength solutions, because the linear relation between load and deformation ceases to apply beyond the elastic limit, and the theory becomes very complicated. This is still true today, and although great progress has been made in ultimate strength design in recent years, the elastic theory provides the more complete coverage (see Section 3.9).

Whether the design is based on the elastic deformation of the beam or on its ultimate strength, the most economical section is the one in which the majority of the fibres are at the greatest distance from the neutral axis, so as to give the longest possible arm to the resistance moment. This gives a great advantage to the fabricated over the natural material, and the stage has now been reached where I-sections because of their extensive use have become cheaper than many structurally less efficient sections of simpler shape. On the other hand, the high cost of the rolls required for shaping steel sections has enforced standardization to a limited range of sections. The geometrical properties of these sections have been carefully computed, and the completeness of the tables has undoubtedly been one of the factors contributing towards the popularity of steel as a structural material.

The beams in a conventional structural steel frame are designed on the assumption that they are simply supported at their ends (*see* Fig. 3.8). This leads to an easy method of assessing the bending moments due to the loads acting on the beams. Since there is no moment at a free support, the bending moment acting at any section is obtained by taking moments about that section of all forces acting on one side of it (Fig. 2.4).

This method of calculating the bending moment is not entirely correct. The much heavier cast iron girders were frequently seated freely on load bearing walls, and this form of support is still employed today for some precast concrete beams. Steel girders, on the other hand, are normally anchored to their supports by bolts or welds, and the connection may be further stiffened by a substantial cleat. The introduction of additional restraints renders the structure statically indeterminate (*see* Sections 3.8 and 3.9).

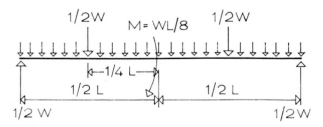

Fig. 2.4. The bending moment in a simply supported beam is obtainable from the conditions of equilibrium alone.

$$M = \tfrac{1}{2}\,W \cdot \tfrac{1}{2}\,L - \tfrac{1}{2}\,W \cdot \tfrac{1}{4}\,L = \tfrac{1}{8}\,W L$$

2.5. *Buckling*

Columns can fail in two entirely different ways. If a short column of steel is overloaded, the material is squashed out of shape, and it does not recover its original shape. The load at which failure occurs depends only on the yield stress of the material, i.e. the stress at which it begins to deform visibly.

A column with a very high ratio of length to thickness, generally referred to as a long column, shows an entirely different type of behaviour. On being overloaded it buckles sideways, but the material remains elastic, the original shape is recovered on unloading, and the column is not damaged by the failure. Its load-bearing capacity is, however, limited by its resistance to buckling (Fig. 2.5). The solution of the buckling failure was published by Leonhard Euler in 1757 [B10]. Mathematically it is one of the most complicated problems in the elementary theory of structures, and

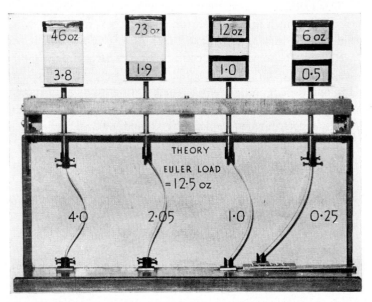

Fig. 2.5. Buckling of "long" columns with various types of end restraint. No permanent damage results (Architectural Science Laboratory, University of Sydney).

Fig. 2.6. Buckling of a column in a steel frame building in Sheffield, England, due to an air-raid in 1940. The temporary shoring for the building is visible on either side of the column.

it is curious that it is the oldest structural formula still in use today. It shows that the buckling load depends only on the modulus of elasticity of the material and on the slenderness ratio of the column, i.e. the ratio of length to thickness. The buckling load is independent of the strength of the material. This means that a material with a low modulus of elasticity, like aluminium, is much more liable to buckling than, say, steel. Unfortunately metallurgical improvements in metals which greatly increase their strength do not alter the modulus of elasticity, so that high strength steel buckles at the same load as mild steel.

In actual fact steel columns are neither so short as to fail purely by yielding, or so long as to fail purely by buckling; the actual failure involves both phenomena (Fig. 2.6). This combined failure involves additional mathematical complications, and during the 19th century column formulae were semi-empirical. During the 20th century a more accurate design procedure has been made possible by extensive tabulation.

The effect of buckling is not limited to columns. In beams the crinkling of the compression flanges and of the web present serious problems. Many of the early failures of iron structures were due to these secondary effects. The first detailed study of this problem was made by William Fairbairn and Robert Stephenson during the construction of the two tubular bridges over the River Conway and the Menai Straits in Wales in 1845 [B12, p. 291]. These bridges consisted of thin-walled rectangular tubes through which the trains ran, as in tunnels. Fairbairn reported that "some curious and interesting phenomena presented themselves in the experiments. Many of them are anomalous to our preconceived notions of the strength of materials, and totally different to anything yet exhibited in any previous research. It has invariably been observed, that in almost every experiment the tubes gave evidence of weakness in their powers of resistance on the top side, to the forces tending to crush them". These experiments led to the use of reduced working stresses in compression and the employment of stiffeners, both devices still in use today.

2.6. The Re-Discovery of Concrete

The origins of concrete construction, like those of so many other building techniques, can be traced back to Roman work carried out two thousand years ago. Roman concrete consisted mainly of broken brick embedded in lime mortar (*see* Section 1.2). Due to the excellent workmanship, aided by the chemical action of the brick dust, much of the work has survived in spite of the weakness of the lime mortar.

Occasionally a volcanic ash from Mt. Vesuvius, found at Pozzuoli (pozzolana cement) was mixed with the lime, and this material bears a closer resemblance to modern cement; in particular it ,is unlike ordinary lime, waterproof, and therefore more durable when exposed to the weather.

The Romans employed wooden formwork, and the marks may still be seen, e.g. on the Pantheon (*see* Fig. 1.1). Use was made of hollow pots cast into the concrete to reduce the dead weight, as in a modern hollow-tile floor, e.g. in the tomb of Empress Helene near Rome. There are even a few instances of the use of metal bars (usually bronze) embedded in the concrete, e.g. in the roof of the Baths of Caracalla in Rome.

Concrete fell into disuse after the fall of the Roman Empire, and it was rediscovered as a result of a systematic investigation by J. Smeaton preceding the reconstruction of the Eddystone Lighthouse off the Plymouth coast. This lighthouse, on the main shipping route to North America, had been twice destroyed because of its exposed position. Smeaton eventually relied on joining the stones with an elaborate system of mortice-and-tenon joints. However, his report, published in 1793, provides the basis for the manufacture of water-resistant cement. After burning lime from a number of deposits, he found that the properties characteristic of Roman pozzolana could be obtained from some "dirty" limes, i.e. limes with an admixture of clay which had hitherto been considered unacceptable.

In 1796, J. Parker was granted a patent for a natural hydraulic cement, made by "burning noddles of clay containing veins of calcareous matter", found near London, which he called Roman cement. The name was presumably chosen for its advertising value, as was the name Portland cement given by J. Aspden to the first artificial cement in 1824.*

---

* Portland stone, an Upper Jurassic oolitic limestone from South West England, was, at that time, highly esteemed for its fine grain, even colour and easy workability. Stucco on brick, painted to look like it, was used in many of the terraces and squares of London for which Portland stone was too expensive. Since maintenance was a major factor, the use of a waterproof cement was undoubtedly desirable. Aspden has been criticized in recent years on the ground that the disagreeable colour of Portland cement bears no resemblance to the famous stone; but he did not suggest that it should be used without paint, and in the circumstances of his time, the use of the name is within the limits of fair advertising. At any rate it has been accepted into every language.

Parker's cement depended on limited deposits of naturally pre-mixed material. Portland cement is made by burning together finely divided limestone and clay (or shale), and it can be made almost anywhere. The first factories for Portland cement outside the British Isles were opened in France in 1840, in Germany in 1855, in the U.S.A. in 1871, and in Australia in 1889.

2.7. The Beginnings of Reinforced Concrete Construction

Plain concrete was used extensively as a structural material in public works during the 19th century, including bridges spanning over 200 ft. [B37].

The adoption of concrete as an architectural material was much slower, and there are few examples of unreinforced buildings. At first its main use in building construction was as infilling over brick jack arches to form the floor of industrial buildings. In 1845 W. Fairbairn, who contributed greatly to the development of fireproof factory construction, designed an eight-storey factory in Manchester in which the floors were supported by concrete in place of the usual brick [B17]. The jack-arches were much shallower and their span much greater than that of contemporary brick arches, and the wrought iron plate may have served to some extent as tension reinforcement; but Fairbairn presumably conceived the floor as a plain concrete arch.

Reinforced concrete is essentially a French invention. It is usually credited to Joseph Monier, who took out a patent in 1867 for the manufacture of reinforced concrete flower pots. Two other Frenchmen have a prior claim: J.-L. Lambot, who designed a boat of reinforced concrete for the Paris International Exhibition of 1855, and François Coignet, who took out a patent for the construction of concrete floors in 1861 [B31]. However, it was Monier's ability in publicizing the new method which established reinforced concrete as an important new method of construction, and a great deal of the important work in the late 19th and early 20th centuries was done under his patents. The other two most important patentees were François Coignet's son Edmond, and François Hennebique.

Hennebique's British Patent No. 30,143 of 1897 states clearly in the opening clauses the advantage claimed: –

"The use of strengthened beton in buildings has within recent years greatly developed. It has been thought possible by mixing beton and iron or steel to replace the purely metallic elements of building construction by parts equally incombustible but lighter and more simply and rapidly made. In any case the mixture of cement or hydraulic lime which resists perfectly compression, with iron or steel which more particularly resists tension and flexion, has not hitherto been capable of being carried out in a judicious and rational manner."

The acceptance of reinforced concrete in architecture was slow, and there are few complete buildings dating from the 19th century. An early American example is the Ward House at Port Chester, New York (R. Mook, Architect), built in 1873 entirely in concrete and still standing [B33]. This is, however, an isolated case, the owner asking for a completely fireproof residence.

Architecturally prominent structural members were, however, common; e.g. the magnificently curved reinforced concrete stair-case at the Petit Palais, in the Champs-Elysées, 1898, (C. Girault, Architect, and F. Hennebique, Engineer and Builder) [B31].

Tony Garnier suggested its use in 1902 as his Project for an Industrial City, and in the early 20th century it was discussed as the architectural material of the future [B17]. However, Auguste Perret, who used it for the first time in 1903, remained for many years the only architect to employ concrete freely on important work [B33]. Prior to the acceptance of the modern style in architecture, reinforced concrete remained largely the preserve of the engineer.

By the end of the 19th century 43 different patent systems were used in England [B27]; of these 15 were originally patented in France, 14 in Germany or Austria-Hungary, and 8 in the United States. Some employed complex and highly original systems of reinforcement, in others the arrangement of the reinforcement was similar to that in use today (Fig. 2.7). In the end, the simplest arrangements of the reinforcement proved as effective as the more complicated systems, and they were more economical in labour.

From 1885 the Monier patents were being exploited in Germany and Austria-Hungary by the firm of Wayss and Freitag, and several hundred reinforced concrete bridges were built during the next five years. Professors E. Mörsch and C. Bach, with financial support from this firm, carried out one of the most extensive structural engineering research programmes of all time, which established most of the fundamental properties of the new materials (Fig. 2.8).

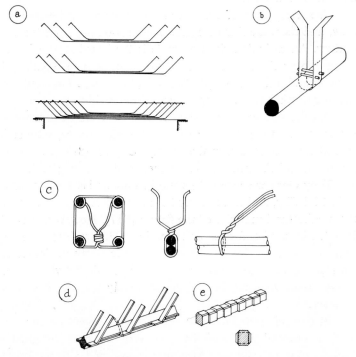

Fig. 2.7. Special patent reinforcing bars used at the turn of the present century. (a) Coignet bent-up bars (French); (b) Hennebique stirrups (French); (c) B.R.C. hooping and stirrups (British); (d) Kahn Bar (American); this was used in the Melbourne Public Library, the first major Australian reinforced concrete building; (e) Indented Bar (British). (From H. J. Cowan, *The Design of Reinforced Concrete*, Sydney, (1963).)

 (a)

 (b)

Fig. 2.8. Failure of reinforced concrete beams (a) by initial yielding of the steel (primary tension failure) when there is a small amount of reinforcement; and (b) by initial crushing of the concrete (primary compression failure) when there is more reinforcement. Failure ultimately always occurs by disintegration of the concrete. (Department of Civil Engineering, University of Sheffield.)

The firm also commissioned K. Koenen to deduce a system of computation, published in 1886 [B28]. Koenen assumed that plane sections remain plane, and neglected the tensile strength of the concrete, as is still done at the present time; but being unable to determine the position of the neutral axis, he placed it in the centre of the cross-section. This error was corrected in 1894 by Edmond Coignet and Napoléon de Tedesco in a paper presented to *Société des Ingénieurs Civils de France*, which is the basis of the present theory.

Experimental evidence shows that plane sections in reinforced concrete, in spite of the cracks on the tension face, remain essentially plane after bending, as in steel beams. The relation between the maximum compressive strain in the concrete and the tensile strain in the steel can therefore be derived from the geometry of the beam. In elastic design, the stresses in the steel and the concrete are obtained from Hooke's Law. The location of the neutral axis depends on the designer. If he uses a large quantity of steel, the controlling factor is the compressive stress in the concrete. As the amount of reinforcement is reduced, the tensile stress in the steel becomes the controlling factor, and the neutral axis moves towards the compression face.

Reinforced concrete being composed of two materials, the mathematics of its theory is more complex than for a single material. However, the principle is essentially simple, and the apparent complexity of the equations is superficial and not important in practice.

The solution has been greatly simplified by design charts and tables. Although the designer's task is not as simple as in the case of structural steel, this is mainly due to the difficulty of standardizing reinforced concrete sections. The ability to vary reinforced concrete freely to suit the architectural requirements of the building is also one of its great advantages, since it allows the designer to decide on a size of concrete section desirable from aesthetic and planning considerations, or the requirements of the other constructional details, and then provide the requisite strength by suitable reinforcement. In addition, reinforced concrete provides the body as well as the skeleton of the building.

The assessment of the resistance moment of reinforced concrete sections is therefore not the main problem posed by the reinforced concrete and frame building, and the real difficulty arises from the continuity of the structure. Since the beams and the columns are normally cast in one piece, bending moments are transmitted from each beam to the adjacent beams and also to the columns.

Attempts have been made to solve this problem by devising a series of empirical moment coefficients relating the load acting on the beam or column to the maximum bending moment produced by it. While this method, still widely in use, has the undoubted merit of simplicity, it gives sometimes an entirely erroneous answer. In view of the complexity and importance of this problem, it is not surprising that it has given rise to a vast number of books and technical papers, and numerous methods have been proposed during the last fifty years (*see* Sections 3.8 and 3.9).

Chapter 3

Two-Dimensional Structures, and the Development of the Rigid Frame Theory

You must learn to think as the structure thinks.
Hardy Cross [B.19]

3.1. Timber Trusses and Steel Trusses

Beams and lintels have evident limitations for long spans; depth is needed to carry loads across a considerable distance, and this can only be achieved by the use of deep beams which are heavy and extravagant in the use of material, by arches which exert a horizontal thrust difficult to accommodate at a great height above the ground, or else by trusses (*see* Fig. 4.4).

In spite of the modest part played by timber structures in traditional construction, they are properly the fore-runners of modern structural techniques. Timber roofs, similar to those used in modern domestic construction, have been built from the very earliest times. The Romans built timber structures of longer span, although none survive. Trajan's column in Rome, for example, shows a bridge with a wooden superstructure built by Appollo-dorus of Damascus across the Danube in Roumania [B11]; the river may have been narrower in Roman days, but it must have been many hundreds of feet in width.

This form of construction was revived during the Renaissance by Palladio, who built several timber bridges exceeding 100 ft. in span (Fig. 3.1). Records of old timber bridges are necessarily incomplete, but it is evident that the 19th century could look back on a long tradition of timber bridge truss construction.

Since the theory of the statically determinate truss is one of the simplest problems in structural mechanics, and all the elements for a solution were available in the 16th century, it is surprising that no serious attempt towards scientific design was made before the 19th century. The impetus was provided by the needs of the railways, whose construction commenced in 1821. The entire problem was solved between 1830 and 1860.

The building of the railways posed a new problem because of the number and the size of the bridges required in a very short time. The railway train is incapable of negotiating steep gradients uphill or downhill, nor can it operate until the permanent way is complete.

In Western Europe, where the first railways were built in densely populated areas, the bridges were of a permanent character, and stone arches and cast iron girders or arches were mainly used. Considerable emphasis was often placed on the need for the engineering work to blend with the landscape.

In America and in Russia the sparse population and the long

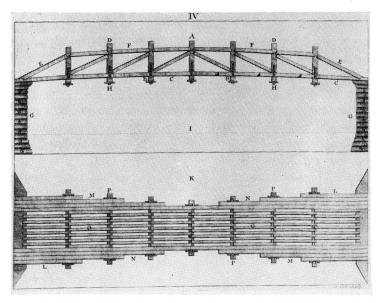

Fig. 3.1. Timber bridge. (From *The Architecture of A. Palladio*, translated by G. Leoni from the Manuscript in Worcester College, Oxford, A. Ward, London 1742.)

distances enforced economy in initial expenditure, and timber trusses were used during the early years. Howe's trusses, still known by his name, were similar to Palladio's, except that iron was substituted for the tension members; this reduced the weight and eliminated some of the expensive timber-to-timber joints. After 1840 bridges of the same type were built entirely in wrought iron, and the cost of the material made scientific methods of design imperative. Failures were not uncommon, although they were more frequently due to inadequate bracing or to buckling of the compression members than to an inadequate quantity of material [B14].

3.2. The Theory of Statically Determinate Structures

The first analysis of the truss was given by Squire Whipple, an American bridge builder from Utica, N.Y., in 1847. In 1850 D. J. Jourawski, a Russian railway engineer, produced the method of Resolution at the Joints, whereby the forces in the members are obtained by considering the conditions of equilibrium at each joint in turn; this did not, however, become known in the West until Karl Culmann, professor at the Zurich Polytechnic, published it independently a few years later [B16].

In 1862 the German engineer A. Ritter produced another analytical approach, the Method of Sections. Ritter cut the truss along an imaginary line, and replaced the internal forces by equivalent external forces. By making a sufficient number of cuts and taking moments about convenient points, the magnitude of the forces can be obtained.

In 1864 Clerk Maxwell, at that time Professor of Physics and Astronomy at Kings College, London, published the well-known graphical solution of the reciprocal stress diagram (Fig. 3.2). This is one of the most remarkable contributions to structural mechanics. It is so simple that many architects remember it when they have forgotten most of their structural theory, and it was made by a man who had no direct connection with structures or even with engineering, but is best-known for his theory of electromagnetism.

The three principal methods for the analysis of plane trusses were therefore developed in a period of less than twenty years, after centuries of truss design by empirical methods. It demonstrates how an urgent need can act as a stimulus.

All these theories are based on the assumption that the members of a truss are pin-jointed. The early trusses were, in fact, connected in this manner. For example, the truss patented in England by James Warren in 1848, and still known by his name, originally consisted of cast iron compression members, with holes

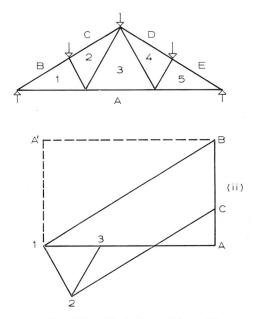

Fig. 3.2.   Clerk Maxwell's Reciprocal Stress Diagram.

Let us consider the equilibrium of the left-hand support. The reaction AB, the internal force in the rafter B1 and the force in the horizontal tie A1 must balance, since the joint is not in motion. We know the magnitude and direction of the reaction, and we can represent it by the vertical line AB. We know the direction of the internal forces, and we can draw lines parallel to them. These intersect to complete the triangle B–A–1; it is not necessary to complete the parallelogram of forces by drawing 1–A′–B. Further triangles and polygons of forces are then drawn for each joint in turn, and their combination gives the "reciprocal stress diagram", from which the internal forces are scaled.

for the pins embodied in the casting, and wrought iron tie bars forged to form eyes at the ends, the members being connected by pins and cotters. The pinned connections were in time replaced by rivetted, bolted, or welded joints, which no longer permitted free rotation of the members. However, if the members are sufficiently flexible to permit the requisite deformation of the truss, the disturbance is mainly in the vicinity of the joint, and it is normal practice to treat trusses as "pinned" unless the connections are unusually rigid.

3.3. Conditions for Statical Determinateness

The simplest plane frame consists of three pin-jointed members. If extra joints are to be added to this elementary frame, two additional members are required for each pin. As Professor Möbius showed in 1837 [2.2], the number of bars required for a pin-jointed frame is therefore

$$n = 2j - 3$$

where j is the number of pin-joints.

If fewer members are used, the frame can be deformed by the slightest load; it is in fact a mechanism and not a structure. If more members are used, the structure becomes more rigid; but there are more forces than can be determined by the simple laws of statics, and the structure becomes statically indeterminate. In order to obtain a solution, it is necessary to consider in addition to the statical equilibrium either the elastic deformation of the frame (elastic design), or else its mode of collapse (ultimate strength design). The amount of work involved depends mainly on the number of redundant members, i.e. members which are additional to those required for a statically determinate structure (*see* Section 3.9). For a large number of redundant members the amount of work is very considerable, and an accurate design may require the aid of a computer or a mechanical model (*see* Sections 4.1 to 4.3).

Since the statically determinate structure is a mechanism with one additional member, this last member is bound to fit. If the setting out is slightly inaccurate it is still possible to assemble the frame without undue force; although the frame would not be quite true to shape, this may not be a serious matter.

In a statically indeterminate frame the redundant members must be exactly true if they are to be fitted without force. This is particularly difficult in large precast concrete frames, for which a statically determinate design is more satisfactory in practice.

3.4. Prestressing

On the other hand, it may be advantageous to introduce deliberately members which are too long or too short, and force them into position with a hydraulic jack or a turnbuckle, as the case may be. The frame is then stressed before any load is applied, and if these stresses are mainly opposite to those produced by the load, the load carrying capacity of the structure is increased. This form of prestressing was used in many of the early trusses, usually on an empirical basis. The theoretical solution was obtained by Castigliano in 1870 (see Section 3.8) [B18]. Today it is not uncommon to use a prestressing cable between the supports which forces the structure off its supports and thus serves the double purpose of simplifying the removal of the formwork and improving the stress-distribution in the structure by superimposing initial stresses on the stresses due to load. Since the structure begins to carry its own weight as soon as it lifts off the supports, it is actually possible to combine stresses due to load and due to prestressing, each being in excess of the permissible stress, provided that they are of opposite sign (Fig. 3.3).

While prestressing has occasionally been used in steel structures, its main advantage is in conjunction with concrete, which is much stronger in compression than in tension. By superimposing an appropriate eccentric compression it is possible to remove the tensile stresses due to bending and so obtain a structure free from the haircracks which inevitably occur in normal reinforced concrete. This was realized as early as 1886, when C. W. F. Doehring, in

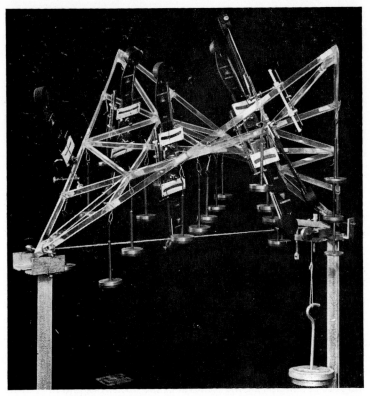

Fig. 3.3. Perspex model of a triangulated saddle frame prestressed across the lower supports by a nylon tendon. (Architectural Science Laboratory, University of Sydney.)

Germany, patented a method for the manufacture of mortar slabs with steel-wire reinforcement. Almost as old is P. H. Jackson's American patent (1888) for inducing preliminary compressive stresses in concrete arches and floor structures by tightening tie rods with the aid of turnbuckles [B35]. The first fundamental treatment of the problem was published in 1907 by K. Koenen, who had proposed the first theory for normal reinforced concrete in 1886.

All the early attempts at prestressing concrete failed because in the 19th century the nature of shrinkage and creep were not properly understood. The prestress disappeared almost entirely after a period of time since the concrete was too weak and the prestress too low.

When concrete hardens, some of the water with which the dry components are mixed is lost by evaporation and some combines chemically with the cement, and as a result the concrete shrinks by approximately one part in three-thousand. This causes an equal contraction in the prestressing steel and an appreciable loss of prestress. A change in length of steel by 1/3000 produces a change in stress of approximately 10,000 pounds per square inch, more than half the stress admissible in 19th century reinforcing steels. More than half the prestress is thus dissipated by shrinkage alone. There is a further loss due to creep, since the prestressing force acting over long periods tends to squeeze more water out of the pores of the material, with consequent further contraction of the concrete and the prestressing steel.

Eugène Freyssinet first appreciated this problem in the nine-teen-twenties and began experiments with very high-strength concrete prestressed with piano wire. With prestresses ten times those previously employed, he reduced the loss to a little over ten per cent. The use of high-tensile steel is thus a necessity for prestressed concrete.

Steel with the high strength suitable for prestressing cannot be employed in normal reinforced concrete. The concrete extends with the steel and the cracks become excessive when the steel stress exceeds about 30,000 pounds per square inch. This limitation does not apply to prestressed concrete which is designed to be free from cracks, so that there is no upper limit to the permissible steel stress apart from that imposed by the potentialities of steel fabrication. It is therefore possible to supply the resultant tensile force in the section with a much smaller cross-sectional area of steel, and the resulting steel economy was the principal reason for the rapid development of prestressed concrete immediately after the Second World War when steel was in short supply. A large number of methods have been patented [B34], as in the early days of reinforced concrete.

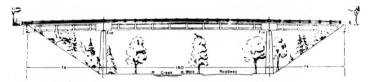

Fig. 3.4. Walnut Lane Bridge, Philadelphia, 1949, the first major prestressed concrete bridge in the U.S.A. The centre span is 160 ft., simply supported.

At present the high cost of prestressing does not compensate for the economies over the relatively short spans encountered in buildings, and most of the applications of prestressed concrete are in bridge construction (Fig. 3.4). However, for shells it has the added advantage that it lifts the structure off the formwork (*see* Chapter 4).

3.5. *Advantages of Statically Indeterminate Structures*

Any statically determinate structure can be made redundant by introducing stiff joints, additional members, or additional reactions. The reverse process can be achieved by introducing additional pin-joints.

An additional support adds a redundancy in the same way as an additional member. A rigid joint, e.g. a joint in a monolithic concrete structure or a joint in a steel structure stiffened with a substantial cleat, also adds a redundancy to the frame. The introduction of an extra pin, on the other hand, removes a redundancy (Fig. 3.5).

The choice between the statically determinate and the redundant structure depends on a number of factors. The redundant structure, being stiffer, is more resistant to earthquakes, explosions and aerial attack. On the other hand, the members of the statically determinate structure fit even if slightly over- or under-size; changes in dimensions due to temperature or moisture-movement can be absorbed without causing additional stresses, and stresses due to uneven settlement are avoided.

The maximum bending moments in redundant frames are

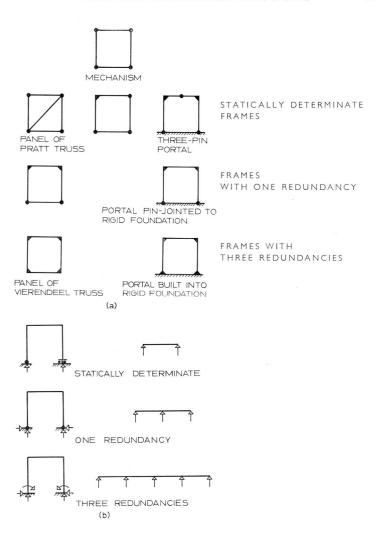

Fig. 3.5   (a) The simple square frame. A pin-jointed square frame is structurally unstable. It can be rendered statically determinate by a diagonal or a rigid joint, or alternatively two rigid joints coupled with an extra pin. A rigidly jointed square panel has three redundancies. (b) Comparison of a portal frame with a continuous beam. The effect of adding additional rigid joints is the same as adding additional reactions. Statically determinate frames. Frames with one redundancy. Frames with three redundancies.

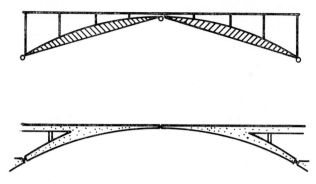

Fig. 3.6. The characteristic shape of Maillart's bridges results from the junction of the three-pinned arch with the road slab. Since the arch is three pinned, the maximum bending moment occurs approximately at quarter span, where the section is thickest.

generally lower; however, this is not an important consideration if it is possible to design a statically determinate frame so as to produce the maximum bending moment at a joint where extra depth can easily be provided. The appearance of strength and simplicity of Maillart's bridges [3.1] is based on this principle (Fig. 3.6).

Fig. 3.7. Railway bridge over the Firth-of-Forth, near Edinburgh, 1883. (Engineer: Sir Benjamin Baker). It is 8,200 ft. long, with a maximum clear span of 1,710 ft., and consists of three double cantilevers which support short intermediate spans.

In general, the statically determinate structure is preferable if there are no good reasons for the use of a redundant structure since it is less affected by secondary stresses and is much simpler to design; the latter consideration has, however, lost much of its importance today when there are numerous standard solutions and mechanical aids to design.

The early long-span steel structures were almost invariably statically determinate. The statically determinate version of the beam continuous over a number of supports is the cantilever girder, which was first employed on a grand scale in the Firth-of-Forth Bridge (Fig. 3.7), to this day one of the masterpieces of bridge building. By introducing two pins into the span which supports a short girder, the beam is rendered statically determinate. This method has been used extensively in recent years in precast concrete frame buildings, where the "pin" can be produced by a scarf joint which permits the requisite rotation.

The statically determinate version of the rigid frame is the three-pin portal. There being no bending moment at the top pin, the horizontal reaction can be determined by taking moments about this pin, and the vertical reactions are obtained in the usual way. The Galeries des Machines, built for the Paris International Exhibition of 1889, consisted of a series of three-pinned portals with a span of 375 ft. (Engineer: Contamin; Architect: Dutert [B17].) It was unfortunately demolished.

3.6. Continuity

The Firth-of-Forth Bridge and the Galeries des Machines, in spite of their great span, are basically simple structures. Their impressiveness is due largely to the clear expression of the structure. The structural problem becomes much more complex in the ordinary steel frame building.

It is generally assumed that the steel skeleton is statically determinate if rivetted or bolted connections are used because they are relatively flexible. For vertical loading, the columns are then considered as if cantilevering from the ground, with the beams simply supported between them (Fig. 3.8).

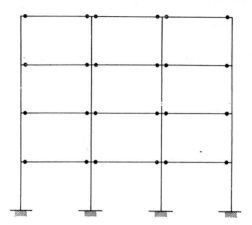

Fig. 3.8. In the "simple" design of steel frames under dead load the beams are considered simply supported on the column cleats.

This simple picture is unsatisfactory for a number of reasons. Whether the lightest possible connections are employed or a substantial stiffening cleat is used, the connections have some rigidity which causes redistribution of bending moments, and induces stresses in the columns and at the ends of the beams for which no allowance is made in simple design. The behaviour of structures with semi-rigid connections has been the subject of extensive investigations by the Steel Structures Research Committee in England in the late nineteen-twenties [3.2].

Secondly, in any multi-storey building the steelwork must be protected against fire. Although lightweight fireproofing is now used to an increasing extent, the predominant method is encasement in solid concrete, which produces a frame with the same rigidity as a reinforced concrete skeleton [B29]. In fact, the concrete carries so much of the load that the stresses in most of the steel members are only a small fraction of those obtained from an analysis of the bare steel frame [3.3]. It is not at present considered safe to allow for the effect of the concrete encasement, except by assuming increased resistance to buckling, because the uncased frame must have adequate strength during construction, and subsequently the casing may not always have perfect bond with the steel. However, the designer who regards solid concrete encasement as an old-fashioned form of protection can substitute a reinforced concrete frame for the smaller buildings, or use lightweight fire-proofing for the taller ones to obtain a lighter structure.

It is more difficult to devise a satisfactory method for taking account of the cladding. In a structure with light-weight floors and glass curtain walls the stiffening effect is slight, and special diagonal bracing or shear walls are essential. However, when brick walls and reinforced concrete floors are used, the frame is often capable of resisting a complete reversal of moment and severe overstressing. This is borne out by experimental investigations and by the manner in which buildings stood up to the effect of severe bombing. For example, a ten-storey block of flats with concrete-encased steel frame and brick walls, damaged during an air raid in London in 1941, remained upright, even though the corner stanchion was completely severed [3.4]. While one is tempted by the low stresses recorded in some steel frames to reduce the factor of safety, this could be dangerous in frames which are only lightly clad.

The tendency towards considering the frame as rigid—and ensuring that this ideal is translated into construction—is further reinforced by a consideration of horizontal loads. In earthquake areas lateral forces are always a dominant factor. Wind load becomes important in tall frames.

In addition to horizontal bending of the frame, wind may also induce torsion in a building which is distinctly L-shaped in plan. If buildings of sufficient height and lack of symmetry become common, this effect may have to be included in the standard design process.

Since the problem of resistance to lateral forces cannot be solved by statics alone, it was common practice in the past to assume the location of the points of contraflexure, where the curvature changes from convex to concave, and the bending moment consequently changes from positive to negative. At the point of contraflexure the bending moment is nil, so that a pin can be inserted without affecting the structural behaviour of the frame

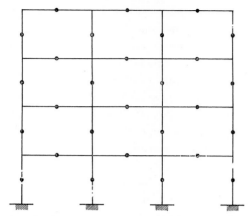

Fig. 3.9. In the "simple" design of steel frames for lateral loading, the location of points of contraflexure is assumed, usually half-way along the column. Since these are points of zero bending moment, they can be treated as "pins", and the frame is thus rendered statically determinate.

under the particular system of loading considered. The frame is thus rendered statically determinate by introducing imaginary pins (Fig. 3.9). However, the picture of the pin-jointed frame is dependent on the assumed location of the pins, and more accurate methods of treating the frame as rigid are gaining ground.

3.7. Theory of Built-in and Continuous Beams

Continuity is therefore a dominating factor in modern frame construction. Its most important effect is not the change in the magnitude of the stresses, which can be accommodated by a very generous factor of safety, but the reversal of their sign. Thus the bending moment in simply supported beams is only positive, and it reduces to nil at the free supports. In continuous beams the moments are reduced, but substantial negative moments appear over the supports where previously there were only small positive moments. This is easily demonstrated by cutting slots in a timber beam. The opening up of the slots indicates tension, and the closing compression.

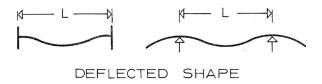

DEFLECTED SHAPE

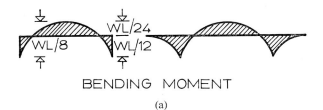

BENDING MOMENT

(a)

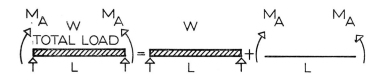

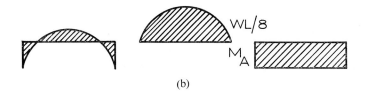

(b)

Fig. 3.10.   Bending Moments in Built-in Beams.

Since the beam is rigidly connected to the supports, its deflected shape must remain horizontal at those points (a—left). The supports impose restraints on the beam which are equivalent to vertical reactions and to fixing moments M_A. The beam behaves therefore in the same way as the central portion of a simply supported beam with cantilever overhangs, which are just long enough to keep the beam horizontal at the supports, and the magnitude of the reactions M_A is therefore equal to that of the cantilever moments (a—right).

The bending moment diagram is thus composed of two parts (b): the usual diagram for the simply supported beam, and a superimposed diagram due to the fixing moments M_A. It can be shown that the area of the parts of the bending moment diagram must be equal, so that the net moment at the support is

$$M_A = \tfrac{2}{3} \cdot WL/8 = WL/12$$

which is also the maximum bending moment.

Continuity is particularly important in reinforced concrete, where an adequate quantity of steel must always be placed on the tension face. In steel construction an unpredicted stress reversal is less serious since the strength in tension and compression is approximately the same.

In its simplest form, the theory of statically indeterminate structures goes back to L. H. M. Navier, who in 1826 (*see* Section 2.3) published the theory of the built-in beam. Although his method, based on quadruple integration of the applied load, has been largely superseded, his basic concept is still valid (Fig. 3.10).

The problem of the continuous beam is somewhat similar. It is assumed that the reactions do not prevent the rotation of the beam at the supports; but each span is subject to restraining moments exercised by the adjacent spans so as to preserve continuity of the curvature of the beam (Fig. 3.11). This yields the Theorem of Three Moments, presented by B. P. E. Clapeyron in a paper to the French Academy of Sciences in 1857.

For several decades this theorem dominated the design of continuous frames, it being assumed that the columns are sufficiently flexible to exercise no appreciable restraint on the continuous floor. True continuous beams are quite rare in building construction, although in bridges pins are introduced to ensure freedom of move-

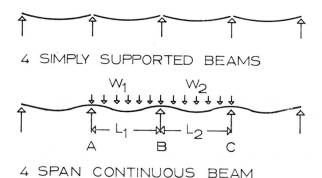

4 SIMPLY SUPPORTED BEAMS

4 SPAN CONTINUOUS BEAM

Fig. 3.11. Simply supported and continuous beam.
Clapeyron's Theorem of Three Moments gives the relation

$$M_A \, L_1 + 2 \, M_B \, (L_1 + L_2) + M_C \, L_2 = -\tfrac{1}{4} \, (W_1 \, L_1{}^2 + W_2 \, L_2{}^2).$$

ment. Where the junction between the floor and the column is rigid, and the stiffness of the column is significant by comparison with that of the floor, the design of a structure as a rigid frame is essential, if only to get a realistic estimate of column sizes, which would otherwise be too small (*see* Section 4.5).

3.8. Theory of Rigid Frames

The first effective method for the design of rigid frames was given by Alberto Castigliano in 1870. It was a remarkable achievement since he presented it as a thesis for his degree to Turin Politecnico at the age of 26. His work had little influence in his time, partly perhaps because he died when only 37 years old, partly also because steel and reinforced concrete were not yet normal structural materials. The examples in Castigliano's book, published in French in 1879, deal with structures built from cast iron and wrought iron [B18].

Castigliano's method is elegant. He determines the strain energy, or total energy stored in the body due to its elastic deformation, and then employs the Principle of Least Work to examine the conditions which make this energy a minimum. Since the differential coefficient of a function is nil when that function passes through a minimum, this procedure gives one equation for each redundancy of the frame. The method is satisfactory when there are only a few redundancies, but it is too cumbersome for the rigid skeleton of a multi-storey building. It remains, however, the best method for curved members, e.g. rigid arches.

The problem can also be approached, as in the Theorem of Three Moments, by considering the deformation of the structure. It is assumed that each right-angled stiff joint remains a right angle after the frame has been deformed by the loads acting on it, and consequently the change in slope of any two members terminating at the same joint must be the same (Fig. 3.12). By this process a series of simultaneous equations are obtained, from which the redundancies can be determined. This approach was originally proposed by Professor Otto Mohr at the Dresden Polytechnikum

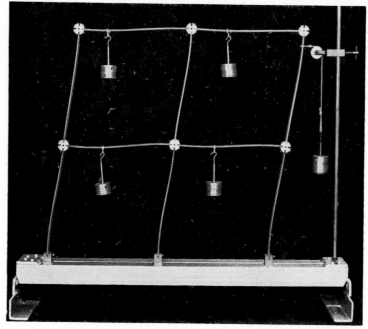

Fig. 3.12.   Solution of rigid frames by considering the deformation. The slope-deflection method [3.5, 3.6], assumes that the rigid joints remain rigid, i.e. right angles remain right angles, however much the rest of the frame deforms. (Architectural Science Laboratory, University of Sydney.)

in 1893. In its present form it was published independently by A. Bendixen in Germany in 1914 [3.5], and G. A. Maney in the United States in 1915 [3.6]. For rectangular frames this slope-deflection method is much more convenient than Castigliano's strain-energy method.

Maney demonstrated the potentialities of slope-deflection analysis by working out a complete multi-storey frame. This was a prodigious feat without modern calculating machinery, and it has since served as a yardstick for other methods of analysis; but it clearly demonstrated that, in spite of the simpler character of the simultaneous equations, their huge number made the method unsuitable for tall multi-bay frames.

Due to the laborious character of these methods, the moments and forces in the great majority of rigid frames during the nineteen-twenties and thirties were determined by semi-empirical methods, frequently standardized by a ruling of a code of practice or building bylaw. The dimensions of the sections were then calculated accurately from these approximate bending moments. One of the dangers of this procedure is the illusion of accuracy created in the mind of the designer by the precision of the second part, which can be no more accurate than the empirical bending moment coefficient. Nevertheless, the method works tolerably well for conventional frames, although difficulties occur with structures having unusual features.

3.9. *Modern Methods of Rigid Frame Design*

The efforts to produce more accurate and less laborious methods have taken four main forms. Attempts have been made to tabulate the bending moments on a number of standard frames, [3.7, 3.8, 3.9], notably by A. Kleinlogel in Germany; however, while it is a simple matter to tabulate all conceivable loading conditions for continuous beams and for single-bay portals and arches, the possible combinations for multi-bay frames are too numerous.

The second attempt is based on the substitution of a process of successive approximations for the precise solution of the simultaneous equations. The Moment-Distribution Method was first proposed by Professor Hardy Cross in a paper given to the American Society of Civil Engineers in 1930 [B19]. Like the slope-deflection analysis it is based on the proposition that a right-angle rigid joint remains a right angle after the structure has deformed. Initially all the joints of the frame are assumed firmly clamped. The beams and the columns are therefore assumed built-in at the ends, and the moments in them are determined accordingly from the standard equations. At most joints this clamping produces unbalanced moments.

In a rectangular frame carrying vertical loads, for example,

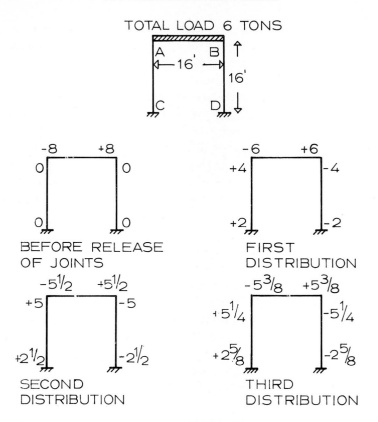

Fig. 3.13. Moment distribution method applied to a single-bay portal built-in at the supports, carrying a uniformly distributed vertical load on the beam. The process of distribution consists of two parts. In the first place the un-balanced moment at the joint must be distributed to the other members framing into the joint. If they are of equal stiffness, the moment is divided equally; if some of the members are bigger, they take a correspondingly larger proportion of the moment. Furthermore, the rotation of the joint induces moments at the far ends of the members. This "carry-over" moment is due to the elastic deform-ation of the members.

In this example, the second distribution reduces the unbalanced moment to 10 per cent, and the third distribution to 2 per cent. An infinite number of distributions is needed to eliminate the error absolutely, although 2 per cent may be considered sufficiently accurate for most purposes.

there are substantial moments in the beams and no moments in the columns. Each of the joints is then released in turn, and the unbalanced moment is distributed to the adjoining members. The process of releasing the joints in turn and distributing the moments can be continued indefinitely, and the unbalanced moments become smaller and smaller. In practice, however, a sufficient degree of accuracy is frequently obtained with three distributions, and two may be satisfactory for a preliminary design. The procedure need not, therefore, be laborious, and it is possible to adjust the amount of work to the importance of the problem (Fig. 3.13).

Cross' method has two great advantages. By comparison with the older forms of analysis, the calculations are much less laborious, and the method can be learned by persons with only limited mathematical knowledge. As a result many consulting engineers accepted it as a standard design procedure, whereas the strain-energy and slope-deflection methods had only been used for major structural problems.

Moment-distribution analysis spread slowly. It was taught in only a few British universities before the Second World War, and became generally known on the Continent only after its conclusion. It is barely mentioned in current Russian text-books.

In spite of the simplification afforded by successive approximations, the arithmetical effort is still considerable. In the immediate post-war years a solution was expected from an abandonment of the elastic theory in favour of ultimate strength design [B25]. While the elastic theory has been the basis of virtually all structural design since the end of the 19th century, failure had always been the criterion in earlier ages (*see* Section 1.5). Even the Romans appear to have carried out load tests to destruction on parts of their structures. The test to destruction is easy to perform and it gives a definite answer; hence it has usually been permitted by building authorities as an alternative to a theoretical analysis. Since the object of structural design is to prevent failure of the structure, this is the more logical way of ensuring its safety.

Tests to destruction on full scale structures, or even on large scale models, are however far too expensive for normal design.

If a complete theory of ultimate strength design could be derived, it would be an important step towards rationalizing structural design.

The basic principle of the design of the steel or reinforced concrete frame for ultimate strength is the same as that of masonry arches in the classical theory (*see* Section 1.4).

Failure of classical structures rarely occurred through damage to the material. Usually they became unsafe when tension between the individual blocks developed, and the joints opened up. The structure then lost stability without overstressing of the stone. The theory is based on ultimate strength, and elasticity has no relevance to structures of this type. Collapse must occur when a sufficient number of "hinges" have formed to turn the rigid structure into a mechanism (Fig. 1.14).

When mild steel reaches its yield point, the strain can be increased without any further increase in stress. Once the plastic yield moment is reached, the steel section therefore forms a "hinge" which allows rotation through an appreciable angle without any further increase in the resistance moment of the hinge section. An increase in the resistance moment occurs only when the steel stress increases again beyond the yield point; however, this "strain-hardening" can usually be ignored in the simple plastic theory.

A structure with n degrees of redundancy requires n plastic hinges to become statically determinate. One further plastic hinge turns it into a mechanism, and it collapses. This is the upper limit which the ultimate load cannot exceed.

The lower limit is represented by the condition of statical equilibrium at which plastic hinges begin to form in the frame. H. J. Greenberg and W. Prager in America proved that the ultimate load must lie between these two limits [3.10]. The problem is therefore by no means simple in a frame with numerous redundancies for which a number of possible collapse mechanisms must be considered.

Although ultimate strength design has now been closely studied for a quarter of a century, particularly at Brown and Lehigh

Universities in the United States [3.11], and at Cambridge University in England [B25], it has proved more complex than was at first anticipated, and the plastic theory applies only if stability failure does not occur prior to the attainment of the ultimate plastic load. It is at present possible to design frames of one or two storeys and a few bays on the basis of ultimate strength, and achieve a solution which is more economical than the elastic design. However, the range of rational design has not so far been extended, and it is doubtful if the plastic theory, once the stability problem is solved, will be simpler than elastic design, although it may produce more economical structures.

It was at first thought that reinforced concrete, because of its brittle nature, would be outside the range of plastic design. If failure is initiated by yielding of the steel, which is usually the case, considerable rotation of the "plastic hinge" is possible without disintegration of the concrete. At present, however, it remains to be proved that the reinforced concrete sections, at which the early "hinges" form, are capable of sustaining sufficient rotation without disintegration to allow the formation of the subsequent hinges in a highly redundant frame. Although the work of G. C. Ernst, of the University of Nebraska, tends to prove this [3.12], the theory is at present limited to very simple frames.

The fourth attempt to produce a less laborious method for the design of rigid frames is perhaps the most encouraging. Even if the theory cannot be reduced to simple terms, the drudgery can be taken out of it by programming a suitable machine to perform the calculations. If this approach proves the answer to the design of multi-storey frames, the consequences may be far-reaching, because the ordinary consulting engineer is unable to afford the necessary equipment, or even the necessary expert knowledge, to operate this form of design. The development of scientific structural analysis in the 19th century led to the emergence of the structural engineer as a specialist consultant to the architect. We may yet witness the emergency of a new specialist consultant to the engineer who provides the detailed solutions for complex structures.

Chapter 4

Three-Dimensional Structures, and the Mechanization of Structural Design

> If a contractor build a house for a man, and does not build it
> strong enough, and the house he build collapses and causes the death
> of the house owner, the contractor shall be put to death.
>
> *Hammurabi's Code, ca. 1950 B.C.* [4.35]

4.1. Digital Computers

The potentialities of automatic computers have been recognized since Charles Babbage in the middle of the 19th Century invented the first calculating machine, which could not merely perform the ordinary processes of arithmetic, but also tabulate the values of any function and print the result. Structural engineers used machines, first hand-operated and later electrified, to an increasing extent after Sir Richard Southwell popularized numerical evaluation by relaxation methods in the forties [4.1]. They never became popular tools for building problems, however, because of the laborious nature of the calculations.

The high speed computer owes its origin to the needs of atomic physicists, electrical engineers, etc.; but because of the ease with which it can be used for repetitive calculations it has significant potential for structural design.

The first high-speed computer ENIAC (electronic numerical integrator and calculator) was developed at the University of Pensylvania in 1946. This was, by present-day standards, slow since the programme was presented to it manually. Since then machines have been provided with automatic storage units which are able to hold programmes in readiness. Mechanical tape or card punches and readers, and teleprinting machines have been added to speed up the operation, and reduce the human effort—and error.

Dr. R. K. Livesley, of Manchester University, wrote programmes for designing structures by computer in 1953 [4.2], and since then an extensive literature has appeared [B43, 4.3].

Electronic digital computers are very fast adding machines which can perform several thousand additions per second. Generally, machines work on the binary system, i.e. they use two digits in place of the customary ten of the decimal system. A hole in the punched tape or card fed into the machine represents one digit, and the absence of a hole the other; this is, however, a mechanical detail which does not enter into its use because the input and output mechanisms are automatically converted into decimals.

The essential features of electronic digital computers are their enormous speed of operation and their "memory", which is capable of storing instructions for performing a sequence of operations in accordance with a standard routine of instructions. While it may well be possible to produce shorter and simpler solutions by other mathematical methods, it is worthwhile to use a computer if it can obtain the result more economically by its arithmetic routines. It is evidently most economical for long repetitive calculations.

All the standard methods discussed in Sections 3.8 and 3.9 can be adapted to mechanical computation, although the slope deflection method has been most frequently used. Generally the simultaneous equations required to determine all the redundancies are written in the form of matrices [4.4], since the computer is particularly well suited for their solution.

The function of the electronic computer is quite different from that of the slide rule, which has had such a profound effect in taking the drudgery out of simple multiplication and division. The slide rule is a portable, inexpensive and essentially personal computer. Electronic digital computers cost tens or hundreds of thousand pounds. At present only a very large structural design organization could maintain its own computer. One could, however, visualize an organization, which could be a commercial firm, a university or a public utility, acting as a consultant to the structural engineer.

Rigid frames cannot normally be designed by direct methods,

and the principal dimensions have to be assumed. It is therefore not practical to try several alternative detailed solutions for an ordinary building, partly because of the expense of manual computation, and partly because it would be intolerably tedious for the designer. With an electronic computer, however, a change in dimensions, even a change from steel to reinforced concrete, calls only for a relatively small change in the instructions, and we might therefore look forward to the possibility of obtaining several solutions in order to ascertain the most economical alternative.

4.2. Analogue Computers

Before a digital computer can be used, a code must be devised which turns the problem into a series of arithmetic operations. This is not always an easy task, and some mathematical equations are more easily solved with the aid of an analogue computer. While all digital computers are based on the same principle, there is a whole range of computers which utilize mechanisms or electrical circuits mathematically analogous to the structural problem. Several were divised in the late 19th century.

Some analogue computers are of general application, i.e. they perform normal mathematical processes, such as multiplication, division, differentiation or integration. The slide rule, for example, is a simple logarithmic analogue.

A number of specialised electrical analogues have been devised for the solution of structural frameworks [4.5]. Most of these consist of electrical circuits, which are adjusted to the general dimensions of the frame and the stiffness of the members by altering electrical resistances. Some analogues can be manufactured for less than a thousand dollars, and they yield a solution fairly rapidly, so that computers of this kind may find a place in the larger design offices.

4.3. Structural Models

The main expense in the use of computers lies in devising a

method of obtaining a solution. Prolonged research may be needed to devise a programme for a digital computer, or to design a special analogue for the particular problem. Computers and analogues are therefore mass-production tools in structural design. The cost of analysis declines rapidly with the number of identical problems to be solved.

Mass production is an essential feature of modern structures. Although no two structures are exactly alike, most conform to a few general types. Rectangular buildings with regular column grids are potentially suitable for computer solution.

"Made-to-measure" structures still have their use, however, and at present computer programmes are not readily adapted to their design. Model analysis is more suitable for unique structures. It is not uncommon to proportion a structure for an important public building in accordance with aesthetic rather than purely structural considerations, or even use a structure of free shape whose geometry cannot be expressed simply in mathematical terms, although this is not advisable for a long-span structure. It is possible to make a guess at the structural dimensions by consulting previous work and exercising common sense; but it is necessary to verify the design for all but the smallest structures. The erection of a full-scale prototype is an expensive check on safety, commonly used in the past, and model analysis may be the only alternative.

When Professor Beggs invented his deformeter in 1922, however, he conceived it more as an analogue [4.6] to reduce the labour of computation, and the likelihood of error in designing rigid frames by the existing strain-energy and slope-deflection methods [B18, 3.5, 3.6].

The instrument is based on a theorem which relates the deflections of a structure at two points and the reciprocal loads at the same points. It was discovered by Clerk Maxwell and published in the *Philosophical Magazine* (Vol. 27, 1864, p. 250) in the same paper which also describes his stress diagram (*see* Section 3.2). The proof of the Reciprocal Theorem was given in 1872 by E. Betti.

The deformeter gives a unit vertical, horizontal or rotational

displacement at a redundant support, and the displacements elsewhere along the model are measured with a micrometer microscope.
The redundant reactions due to a load anywhere on the structure
can then be obtained by the Reciprocal Theorem, and once these
are known the structure becomes statically determinate [B41]. In
retrospect, Begg's method suffered from defects. The insistence on
small deformations, which required a microscope for the measurements, made them unduly laborious, while the acceptance of card-
board as a model material led to errors.

The failure of indirect model analysis to establish itself as
a major design tool is not, however, due to these teething troubles
which were corrected in time through the use of plastic model
materials and the acceptance of large displacements. The perfection
of the moment distribution method by Professor Cross [B19] in the
thirties (*see* Section 3.9), was mainly responsible, because it placed

Fig. 4.1. To determine the redundant reactions of a built-in double-cantilever
arch by indirect model analysis, the arch is given a unit vertical displacement,
a unit horizontal displacement, and a unit rotation; the displacement of the
model at any point gives the corresponding horizontal, vertical and moment
reaction due to a unit load at that point. When the reactions are known, the
structure becomes statically determinate. Alternatively the model can be cut,
and the forces and moments at the cut determined. (Architectural Science
Laboratory, University of Sydney.)

the plane rectangular frame, the most important rigid frame, within easy reach of design by slide rule. The plane curved structure remained as a fruitful field for indirect analysis (Fig. 4.1); however, only two small three-dimensional structures have been analysed by the indirect method [B41] because of the difficulty of measuring their rotation in space.

The further development of model analysis for architectural structures was handicapped by a lack of urgency in developing special facilities, since generally a design can only be used for one building; the spans are moderate in terms of high-strength materials, and the saving in material resulting from an accurate analysis may not equal the cost of the analysis.

The position is quite different in the design of dams, where construction costs are far higher, and in the design of aircraft structures, where saving in weight is essential for operating efficiency. The methods used in direct model analysis have been developed originally for these two types of structure. The investigation for the design of the Boulder Dam, now the Hoover Dam [4.7], led to important developments in the technique of making models, and research on aircraft structures in the early forties was mainly responsible for the invention of miniature strain gauges, such as the electric resistance strain gauge. Both Professor Eduardo Torroja [4.8], and Professor Guido Oberti [4.12], as consultant to Pier Luigi Nervi, used three-dimensional models for direct analysis with mechanical strain gauges in the thirties. The main developments took place in the fifties, particularly in Southern Europe [B42], when electrical instruments came into general use. The first organization specially created for structural model tests was set up in Italy in 1951 [4.9].

In direct model analysis, the strain and deflections of a dimensionally similar model [4.13] are measured, and the corresponding values for the structure are obtained directly by multiplication with a scale factor (Fig. 4.2).

Several other methods of experimental stress analysis have been used in the design of machines and dams, e.g. brittle coatings, photo-elasticity and various optical methods; since 1943 the

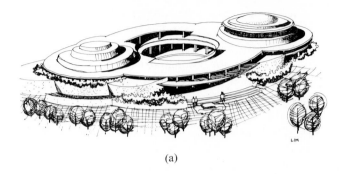

(a)

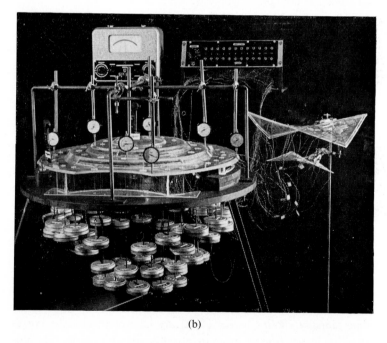

(b)

Fig. 4.2. A perspex model (b) was used to design the folded plate domes for a Club completed in Sydney in 1964 (a). Demountable mechanical gauges were employed extensively to reduce the cost of the test, and electrical resistance gauge were reserved for inaccessible points and points of special importance [4.10]. The measurements served as a basis for locating and proportioning the reinforcement. (Architectural Science Laboratory, University of Sydney.)

Proceedings of the Society for Experimental Stress Analysis, published at present in Westport, Connecticut, have been the principal medium for disseminating new ideas. Only the moiré method, based on interference patterns of two grids, however, has proved of significant value for architectural structures [4.11].

With the rapid advance of digital computer programming it seems possible that the direct method of model analysis may be largely replaced by numerical methods, as the indirect method was overtaken by moment distribution calculations. As a visual aid to structural design, however, model analysis has a permanent place in the evolution of new structural concepts.

4.4. *The Revival of the Three-Dimensional Structure*

In studying the structural principles of the great buildings of the past, we can trace the progress of the post and lintel through the barrel vault to the ribbed vault. Each step reduced the unit weight of the structure—and each step increased the complexity of the design.

A similar development can be traced in modern architecture. The invention of the steel frame at first caused a return to the simplest type of structural framing. It was conceived as a number of vertical and horizontal lines, simply connected: the three-dimensional structure was broken up into a number of one-dimensional elements. This was a rational approach to the problem, since steel is produced in linear form. Although steel allows a great increase in span, the early frame buildings were small by modern standards. When large spans were employed, as in the Galeries de Machines of 1889 (*see* Section 3.5), pin joints were introduced to ensure that the structure was statically determinate.

Although the structure was gradually conceived in two dimensions, particularly with the growing popularity of triangulated trusses, it continued to be treated as statically determinate.

The development of reinforced concrete, because of the rigidity of its connections resulting from monolithic construction, posed new problems. The rigid frame could not be broken up into a number of one-dimensional elements, neither could the forces be determined by statical equilibrium alone.

4.5. *Flat Slabs*

Twentieth-century developments in frame construction emphasised this trend still further. The concrete flat slab floor, patented by Orlando Norcross in the U.S.A. in 1902, dispensed with beams, so that the floor slab performed also the function of the main horizontal structural members. In 1914 J. R. Nichols derived the equation for the sum of the total positive and negative bending moments [4.14], which is still the basis of the present formulae. In 1920 Professor H. M. Westergaard and W. A. Slater

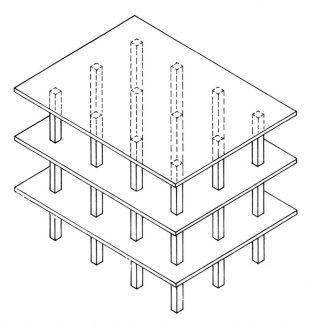

Fig. 4.3. The flat-plate floor reduces the structural frame to its simplest elements, viz. the floor slabs and the supporting columns. Both beams and enlarged column heads are omitted. Although not necessarily the most economical solution, it has the merit of simplicity in construction and neatness in appearance without a false ceiling.

undertook a monumental experimental investigation [4.15], and compared the results with the elastic theory. This led to so-called "empirical" equations for flat-slab design, which have since been adopted in many national codes.

The Westergaard–Slater formulae cease to apply when the enlarged column heads are omitted or replaced by shear reinforcement within the slab (Fig. 4.3), because this was outside the scope of the experiments. This "flat plate" began to make its appearance in America in the early forties, and an elastic method of analysis was developed for it. It divided the structure into two series of frames at right angles to one another, each consisting of the flat plates and the appropriate line of columns. These plane frames could then be analysed by moment distribution, and the three-dimensional structure reduced to two dimensions. The method was included in the 1956 Code of the American Concrete Institute, and the 1958 code of the Standards Association of Australia. An alternative approach, based on ultimate strength, was developed by Professor Johansen in 1943 [B36], and it is now generally admitted for design in Scandinavia and in Russia.

The shear head within the flat plate can be provided by rolled steel sections connected at right angles, and these in turn can be connected easily to steel columns. This paved the way for using steel columns in conjunction with concrete floors, and thus breaking down the division between steel and reinforced concrete construction.

In lift-slab construction, which Phillip Youtz and Thomas Slick introduced in 1950, the concrete slabs are cast on the ground, and subsequently lifted into position. Buildings of more than twenty storeys have been erected by this method.

Due to the absence of beams, the slabs are comparatively thick, and they consequently provide good insulation against fire and sound (*see* Sections 5.11 and 5.12). For the same reason, however, long-term deflection due to creep of the concrete is a problem.

The structural principle of the flat slab has been used occasionally as a form of aesthetic expression. Robert Maillart [3.1] designed in 1910 a warehouse in Zurich in which the column heads blended into the slab in a smooth curve. P. L. Nervi in 1951 used the curves formed by the stress trajectories as a decorative pattern in the Gatti Wool Mill in Rome [4.12]. The majority of structures, however, have emphasised the simplicity of a design composed entirely of horizontal slabs and vertical columns.

4.6. Curved Concrete Structures

Aesthetically more significant has been the revival of curved structures in modern materials, which gained momentum as the limitations of an architecture composed entirely of rectangular blocks became more apparent.

The great structural economy, which can be achieved by the use of curvature, has been appreciated since the days of Ancient Rome. It still applies when modern materials are used, because it is ultimately necessary to offer within the structure a resistance moment equal to the moment of the applied loads. (Fig. 4.4). This requires either curvature or thickness in the horizontal structural members, and over large spans the latter is necessarily associated with heavy weights.

While masonry domes and vaults of the traditional type were still built in the early 20th century, the increased emphasis on engineered construction had already, in the mid-nineteenth century, produced a number of remarkable curved iron structures, such as Joseph Paxton's Crystal Palace in London in 1851 (see Sections 6.3 and 6.6) and Henri Labrouste's Bibliothèque Nationale in Paris in 1868. Iron and steel construction was conceived as an assembly of linear elements formed into curves as required, and this emphasis persisted at the time when the first curved reinforced concrete structures were built. Thus the dome of the Melbourne Public Library, at the time of its construction in 1911 the largest reinforced concrete dome in the world [4.16], was designed as a ribbed structure.

In the following year the completion of the Centenary Hall in Breslau marked a turning point (see Table 4.1). It was the first concrete building which surpassed the Pantheon (see Section 1.2)

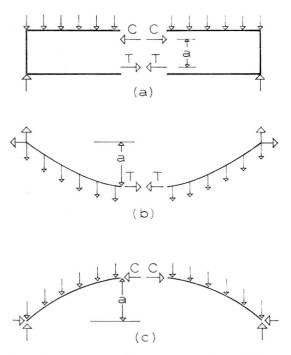

Fig. 4.4. The resistance moment of the structure can be supplied by a moment formed by a tensile and a compressive force acting within the depth of a beam, by a tensile force in a sagging suspension cable, or by a compressive force in a thin arch or shell.

in size (in steel this had been achieved half a century earlier), and for the next forty years there was a marked tendency towards reduction in weight and greater elegance, rather than an increase in span [B37].

It was clear to many of the early reinforced concrete designers that the material had body as well as strength, and could be formed to resist very large forces while at the same time keeping out the weather [B31]. Elimination of the ribs gave a considerable saving in weight and formwork, and also a much neater appearance. The first thin slab structures were arches springing from the foundations so that the horizontal reaction is transmitted directly to the

Fig. 4.5. In Eugène Freyssinet's Aircraft Hangar at Orly, France, built in 1921 and spanning 260 ft.; bending is resisted by the corrugations in the shell.

ground (Fig. 4.5). The structure has architectural limitations because the space near the supports is largely wasted; however, it is only a short step from here to the membrane structure which aims at the elimination of bending stresses.

4.7. The Development of the Membrane Theory

A really thin shell cannot be produced if there are substantial flexural stresses. The internal resistance moment of a section is formed by the flexural tension and compression, and the lever arm between their lines of action. The shell has to be thick enough to accommodate the lever arm, or else corrugated, in which case the tensile and compressive forces act in alternate corrugations. Corrugations are useful only if the bending is limited to one direction, and they are functionally unacceptable for many buildings.

A thin shell can exist without bending. This is easily demonstrated with a soap film, which is quite stable under tensile, compressive and shear forces acting in the surface of the membrane, but breaks immediately if subjected to bending. Most shells are statically determinate if there are no bending moments, just as pin-jointed triangulated trusses are statically determinate (*see* Section 3.2). Bending moments are induced when freedom of deformation is inhibited and the truss made statically indeterminate. This also applies to shells. In practice a shell cannot be supported to give statically determinate edge conditions; but for some geometric proportions the bending stresses can be restricted to thicker edges, where the shell is supported (Fig. 4.6).

The dome over the Planetarium in Jena was probably the first reinforced concrete structure deliberately designed as a membrane by Dischinger and Bauersfeld in 1923 [B37]. It is only 3 cm (1.2 in.) thick over a span of 53 ft. Being a hemispherical dome, its horizontal reaction is fully absorbed by the hoop tension, which is resisted by the reinforcement within the surface of the shell. This may be contrasted with the heavy weight of the traditional masonry dome (Table 4.1).

While the original statement of the membrane theory is credited to G. Lamé and E. Clapeyron [4.17], the first systematic

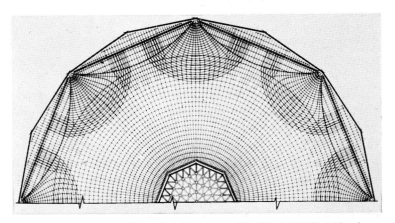

Fig. 4.6.   Stress trajectories and reinforcement of the Market Hall at Algeciras, Spain, designed by E. Torroja, 1933. The polygonal dome spans 156 ft. and is 3½ in. thick, increasing gradually to 18 in. close to the supports to withstand the bending stresses occurring there.

statement of its application to the architectural structures was given by F. Dischinger in a very long chapter on shells in the 1928 edition of the German *Handbuch für Eisenbeton* [4.18]. He derived the membrane stresses from the conditions of equilibrium of the forces acting on an element of the shell, and obtained simple solutions for domes and cylindrical shells based on the circle, parabola, ellipse, catenary and cycloid. F. Aimond added the membrane solution for the hyperbolic paraboloid in 1936 [4.19].

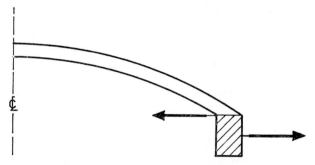

Fig. 4.7.   When a circular dome is less than hemispherical, a ring tie is needed to absorb the horizontal component of the meridional forces. The ring tie consequently expands under load. The hoop forces in the shell are compressive if the angle is small, and the shell consequently contracts. The incompatibility of the deformations of the shell and the ring tie produces bending in the shell near the edges.

The membrane theory applies only if the forces within the shell are compatible with the reactions at its boundaries. This condition is, unfortunately, satisfied in only a few cases. Reverting to the hemispherical shell of the Jena Planetarium, the hoop forces are balanced within the shell, and the meridianal forces (at right angles to the hoop forces) require only a continuous vertical reaction around the circumference of the dome. If the dome is supported on a wall or on a stiff ring girder, the boundary conditions are satisfied. A hemispherical dome, however, has few modern architectural applications and generally a dome with a much smaller angle is used. In a shallow dome the hoop force is still absorbed within the shell; the meridianal membrane force, on the other hand, requires an inclined reaction which is not supplied by the supports in most buildings. It is therefore normal practice to insert a ring tie.

The ring tie, however, creates bending stresses within the shell (Fig. 4.7). In a shallow shell the hoop stresses at the edge of the dome are compressive so that the shell tends to contract on loading; while the tie expands when the dome is loaded. Since the tie is joined to the shell, the shell is subjected to bending, and its thickness must be increased near the edge of the dome to accommodate the flexural stresses. Since the bending stresses depend on the relative elastic deformation of the shell and the tie, they are statically indeterminate.

The same considerations apply to most shell forms with an architectural application. The cylindrical barrel vault, probably the most widely used architectural shell, requires transverse ties for stability in order to absorb the horizontal reaction of the arches at the ends of the shell. In addition longitudinal ties are commonly used to reduce the high longitudinal membrane tension. The elastic deformation of the ties is not compatible with the elastic deformation of the shell, so that bending is introduced in the boundary regions.

In shallow hyperbolic paraboloids a load uniformly distributed in plan gives rise to membrane shear stresses which are uniform over the entire shell. This simple condition is disturbed by the boundaries where framing members are needed to balance the membrane shear, and these in turn give rise to bending.

The bending stresses are frequently significant only near the boundaries and die away rapidly towards the inner portion of the shell. In that case it is possible to design the shell by the membrane theory and increase the thickness of concrete and the quantity of reinforcement empirically in the boundary region.

In "long" cylindrical shells the membrane solution is inadequate even for an approximate design of the shell. Fortunately, the elastic deformation of this important type is sufficiently close to that of a beam spanning between the transverse ties to be designed by the "beam theory" (Fig. 4.8). The concrete at the crown of the shell resists the flexural compression, and reinforcement near the longitudinal edges resists the flexural tension. If the shell has longitudinal ties, the flexural reinforcement can be concentrated there, and the neutral axis is then usually near the top of the tie. The shear force requires diagonal reinforcement in the shell near the supports.

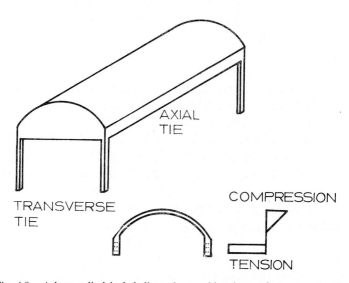

Fig. 4.8.   A long cylindrical shell can be considered, as a first approximation, as a beam. The concrete at the crown resists the flexural compression, and the reinforcement near the longitudinal edges resists the flexural tension.

4.8. The General Elastic Theory of Shells

The membrane theory is related to the general solution in the same way as the theory of statically determinate structures is related to that of rigid frames. Membrane calculations are rarely difficult, but for some shells they are seriously in error. Although elastic solutions exist for most shell forms, the numerical evaluation is often extremely laborious. There is as yet no method comparable in simplicity to the moment distribution analysis of rigid frames.

The most complete solution for domes has been given in Russia by Vlassov; his work has been translated into German [4.20]. Interest in Western countries has concentrated more on cylindrical barrel vaults. The theory commonly used is originally due to F. Dischinger and U. Finsterwalder [4.21]. Several simplifications have been introduced, and those by H. Schorer in America [4.22] and by R. S. Jenkins in England [4.23] have been widely used. There is as yet no generally accepted theory for bending stresses in hyperbolic paraboloids.

Fig. 4.9.   Market Hall at Royan, France, designed by R. Sarger, 1959. A free-shaped dome, 185 ft. diameter, in which the supports merge with the shell.

Tables for the design of cylindrical shells have been produced in America [4.24] and in Germany [4.25]; but they do not yield the solution with the same simplicity as the rigid frame tables of Kleinlogel or Leontovich (*see* Section 3.9). An attempt to derive empirical coefficients from the calculations of existing shells [4.26] is, perhaps, more promising for a simple design method, but is limited in its scope to a narrow range of structures.

A great deal of the drudgery can be avoided by using an electronic computer, but our advances in that direction lag far behind those in the computation of rigid frames [4.27]. Model analysis has advantages for shapes of great complexity, since the cost is largely independent of the mathematical difficulty of the analytical solution [4.10].

The theoretical difficulties have not, however, prevented the construction of shells. Even the early shell structures were remarkably light and graceful [B31, B32, B37, B38, B39].

The main post-war developments are the introduction of prestressing, which further lightens the shell and enables it to be lifted off the formwork; the creation of free shell forms (Fig. 4.9); and a tremendous increase in the maximum span. The most promising of the new shell forms are the hyperbolic paraboloid and the conoid; unlike the dome, both can be formed by straight lines, which greatly reduces the cost of the formwork.

4.9. *Linear Shells*

Although the use of shell roofs has spread rapidly in the last two decades, the high cost of the formwork remains an important objection, and design difficulties have at times been an obstacle. The creation of curved shapes composed of straight or linear elements may therefore be regarded as a constructional advance, rather than as a return to older methods.

It is much harder to trace the beginnings of folded plate construction than to name the first shell roof. In Germany in the nineteen-twenties coal bunkers and similar containers were commonly built from concrete plates monolithically joined without beams, with the reinforcement arranged to conform to the general distribution of moments. Papers on the design of folded plate structures as rigid frames go back to the early nineteen-thirties. Although the theory is basically no more difficult than that of rigid frames composed of beams, the practical application can be very tedious, particularly if the structure is not composed of rectangular plates. The application of moment distribution to folded plates is due to G. Winter and M. Pei [4.28], and many recent design methods have been based on this principle.

Elaborate design methods are not necessarily required. If, for example, the folding is in the nature of a corrugation at right angles to the main span, the structure can be designed as a deep beam or slab from which large portions have been cut away, as in the cantilevered roof of the headquarters of the American Concrete Institute (Fig. 4.10). This alters the geometrical properties of the section; but in a statically determinate structure the bending moments are not affected.

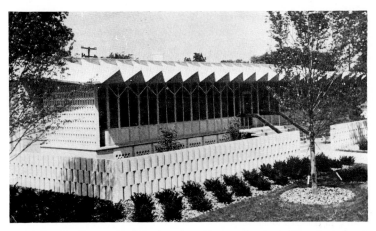

Fig. 4.10. Headquarters of the American Concrete Institute, Detroit, designed by M. Yamasaki (Architect) and C.S. Whitney (Engineer) [4.29]. Due to the small span, 13 ft. 4 in., the precast units are only $3\frac{1}{2}$ in. thick in spite of the bending stresses.

Folded plate structures are not membrane structures, because the bending stresses can never be eliminated, and the thickness of concrete is therefore more than in shells. However, this is not necessarily a disadvantage in small and medium sized structures where the thickness may be determined by considerations of construction or insulation rather than by the magnitude of the stresses.

4.10. Space Frames

While the folded plate structure replaces the shell by a number of flat slabs, the ribbed shell replaces it by a series of linear, if not necessarily straight elements. It varies from the fine mesh of the decorative precast-concrete units employed by Pier Liugi Nervi [4.12], which provide the roof surface, to the coarse grid of the geodesic domes popularized by Buckminster Fuller, which merely provide the skeleton for the roof cover [4.30].

It is debatable whether a structure built in the shape of a shell, but having a greater volume of voids than solid material within the surface, may be regarded as a shell structure. Its overall structural behaviour is that of a shell, but the design of the individual members is determined by the character of the structure as an interconnected frame [4.31]. The ribbed shell is not a true space frame. Although it is three-dimensional, it is a plane structure on a curved surface, and the number of members is less than that required for a space frame.

The simplest statically determinate space frame, the equilateral tetrahedron, has six members joining four points in space. Each additional point in space requires three additional members. The number of members required for the statically determinate space frame is therefore

$$n = 3j - 6$$

where j is the number of joints.

Since it is impractical to draw a stress diagram in space, statically determinate space frames are analysed by a three-dimensional version of the "Method of Resolution at the Joints" (*see* Section 3.2), the Method of Tension Coefficients, proposed by Sir Richard Southwell in 1920 [4.32]. This method gives rise to a large number of simultaneous equations. Until recently this has been a serious objection; but with a computer the answer is readily obtained.

Although a considerable amount of research on the use of space frames for long-span flat roofs has been undertaken in recent years [4.33], the outcome is disappointing so far. The resulting structures show some economy of material, but the architectural potentital differs little from that achieved with plane parallel-chord trusses.

4.11. Suspension Structures

The lightest and most recent of all structural forms, the suspension structure, is the reverse of the shell roof (*see* Fig. 4.4). High-tensile wire ropes provide the requisite tensile force for a much smaller weight than any other material, e.g. about one-tenth of that of mild steel. Buckling is no problem, since the cables are in tension. Bending can be eliminated by making the structure flexible so that it adjusts its shape to that required for pure membrane action. The suspension structure is therefore very light, and

Fig. 4.11. Sidney Myer Music Bowl in Melbourne, Australia (Architects: Yuncken, Freeman Brothers, Griffiths and Simpson). This 40,000 square-foot canopy, built in 1959 with aluminium-bonded plywood supported on flexible galvanized wire ropes, was selected by the American Institute of Architects for the 1959 R.S. Reynolds Memorial Award.

particularly suitable for long spans. Some of the most successful examples have developed from the traditional canvas tent (Fig. 4.11). Aerodynamic stability, however, is a problem which has not yet been fully solved [4.34, pp. 68–103].

Suspension structures were suggested by Frei Otto before 1954 [B40], but few had been built prior to 1958, when they became the dominant structural form at the Brussels International Exhibition. In 1962 a Symposium was held in Paris [4.34] to discuss the theory of design and the experience gained with construction.

4.12. Solution of the Problem of Span

In the technical sense there has been tremendous progress in the first half of the 20th century. The dome of St. Peter's weighed 12,500 lb. per sq. yd.; in the first reinforced concrete dome of greater span, the Centenary Hall in Breslau, built in 1912, this is reduced to a third, and in a modern shell dome to a 50th [B37].

Table 4.1

Building	Construction	Date	Span (ft.)	Weight (lb/sq.yd.)	Per cent
St. Peter's Rome	Masonry dome	1590	137	12,500	100
Centenary Hall, Breslau	Ribbed Reinforced Concrete Dome	1912	215	3,750	30
Market Hall, Algeciras	Reinforced Concrete Shell Dome	1933	160	480	3.8
Schwarzwaldhalle, Karlsruhe	Prestressed Concrete Saddle Shell	1953	240	250	2.0
Le Torneau Hemisphere, Texas	Aluminium Shell Dome	1953	300	41	0.33
C.N.I.T. Exhibition Hall, Paris	Reinforced Concrete Double Shell Dome	1958	720	520	4.1

The largest dome prior to the 19th century, the Pantheon (123 A.D.) spanned 142 ft. Prior to 1958 the greatest dome still had a diameter of only a little over 350 ft. The Paris Exhibition

Hall doubled this with 720 ft. span, without any significant increase in unit weight. Aluminium further reduces the weight, but not the cost, and the use of light metal poses problems in relation to wind and thermal insulation.

There is no apparent advantage in a building of more than 700 ft. span, unless it be to roof an entire city centre, so that the problem of span, which was a main preoccupation of architects from the earliest days of building construction, is now for all practical purposes solved.

Chapter 5

Environmental Design Replaces Structure as the Principal Problem of Architectural Science

> It is probable that all existing whispering galleries, it is certain that the six more famous ones, are accidents; it is equally certain that all could have been predetermined without difficulty, and like most accidents improved upon.
>
> *W. C. Sabine* [5.18]

5.1. The Conflict between Structural Lightness and Functional Efficiency

Structure has been a prime pre-occupation of architects and of connoisseurs of architecture throughout the ages, and many clients, or their architects, have been unable to resist the temptation to span a little longer than the Joneses, because it was a difficult thing to do. In the same way huge precious stones were used in jewellery before excellent imitations became available. To-day the design of a building with a span greater than functionally necessary would be as much of a vulgarity as a necklace with a three-inch imitation diamond.

Spans of several hundred feet and complex structural shapes no longer present insurmountable problems, and the structure of the future building may be distinguished by the elegantly restrained use of the appropriate system, rather than by the flamboyance of some of the early modern buildings.

It seems likely that perfection of the environment will replace structural ingenuity as the primary technical interest of the avant-garde of architects, because in this field we need dramatic developments. At the present time the mechanical and electrical services cost about three times as much as the structure in air-conditioned multi-storey buildings. This is largely because few architects consider the problem seriously at the initial design stage, and the consulting engineer has no alternative but to remedy the deficiencies of the architectural concept with excessive hardware.

Glass walls show up the lightness of the structure; but they seriously complicate the creation of satisfactory lighting and thermal conditions.

Great height dramatically demonstrates the structural potential of the skeleton; but the better utilization of the land does not compensate for the greater vertical transportation cost beyond a certain height.

While these contradictions between structural virtuosity and the creation of a perfect environment are now generally recognized, there are still only a few architects and engineers capable of exercising proper environmental control over the design of building. The use of massive air-conditioning plants to correct an ill-conceived environment does not differ in principle from the use of a masonry façade to hide an unnecessarily ugly concrete structure.

5.2. Climate, Thermal Comfort and the Design of Buildings

Although the scientific study of environmental design is a very recent development, there is a prehistory of architectural climatology, as there is a prehistory of architectural structures. Vitruvius included in the "*Ten Books of Architecture*" [B5] a chapter "On Climate as Determining the Style of the House", and he referred elsewhere to such matters as orientation in relation to the prevailing winds. There is a vernacular construction in terms of the local climate as there is a vernacular construction in terms of the local materials. In Nigeria, light construction, which permits ample ventilation, is used in the humid coastal zone, and thick walls with few windows are used in the arid interior.

While the effect is more noticeable in primitive houses, it can also be found in sophisticated architecture; e.g. when the Renaissance came to Northern Europe, the windows tended to become larger (Fig. 5.1).

Adaptation is far less satisfactory when development proceeds

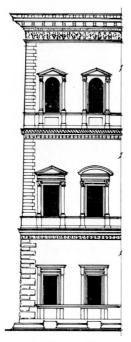 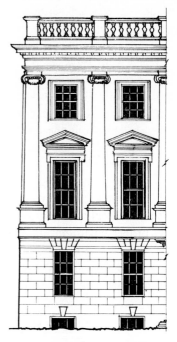

Fig. 5.1. (a) Palazzo Farnese, Rome ca. 1540 (Architects: Antonio da Sangallo and Michelangelo). (b) Lindsey House, Lincoln's Inn Fields, London ca. 1640 (attributed to Inigo Jones).

quickly. In Australia, which has been settled in little more than a century, there is relatively less differentiation between the houses of the humid East Coast and the arid Interior.

Again we could contrast the relatively good adaptation of the Greek temple—originating in a hot climate in the 5th century B.C.—to the cold weather of Northern Europe and Northern America during the Greek Revival of the early 19th century, with the difficulties encountered at first when the Northern European glass curtain wall was employed in warm-weather countries only two decades later.

In terms of modern materials and methods of construction, a better understanding of the inter-relation between outdoor and indoor climate is therefore essential.

Climatic zones are mentioned by Roman and Alexandrian writers. The countries around the Mediterranean Sea are classified as the temperate zone, with a burnt zone in the deserts to the South and a frigid zone in the North stretching as far as Thule. Some writers, e.g. Macrobius (5th century A.D.) assumed another temperate zone in the Terra Incognita south of the Equator, followed by another frigid zone. However, in the Middle Ages this classification became entirely schematic (Fig. 5.2).

Modern climatology began only in the 19th century, and the publication in 1817 by Alexander von Humboldt of his work on Isothermal Lines might be taken as the starting point. During the later 19th century progress was rapid and today records extending over at least a century are available for most major urban centres, which give changes of temperature, humidity, and prevailing winds. Even so, the design of small houses can be complicated by major changes in the microclimate on the top of a ridge or in a hollow. The conditions at the top of a high-rise building cannot always be predicted from ground data, and data collected on top of other

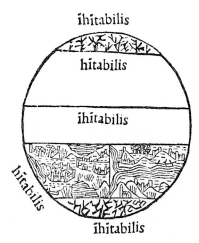

Fig. 5.2. The climatic regions of Sacro Bosco, Professor of Mathematics at the University of Paris. (From *Tractatus de Sphaera Mundi* [5.11]. This popular book was written before 1256, when Sacro Bosco died. It was first printed in Ferrara in 1472, and reprinted about sixty times until the end of the 17th century.)

high-rise buildings are necessarily limited to the last few years, except in some American cities.

Serious studies of the effect of climate on human comfort are even more recent. Again we have an opinion on the subject by Vitruvius: –

"But although southern nations have the keenest wits, and are infinitely clever in forming schemes, yet the moment it comes to displaying valour, they succumb because all manliness of spirit is sucked out of them by the sun. On the other hand, men born in cold countries are indeed readier to meet the shock of arms with great courage and without timidity, but their wits are so slow that they will rush to the charge inconsiderably and inexpertly, thus defeating their own devices. Such being nature's arrangement of the universe, and all these nations being allotted temperaments which are lacking in due moderation, the truly perfect territory, situated under the middle of heaven, and having on each side the entire extent of the world and its countries, is that which is occupied by the Roman people." (*The Ten Books of Architecture* [B5], p. 173).

This view is still widely held after two thousand years, although the preferred environment has perhaps shifted to Paris, London, Los Angeles or Sydney. Physiologists incline to the view [5.1] that *homo sapiens* is best adapted to the hot-humid regions of the tropical forests, and became progressively used to cooler and more temperate climates as he acquired clothing, shelter and heating.

Comfort is a relative term. Humidities which are acceptable and even pleasant while relaxing on the beach, may be intolerable for concentrated work. While we know that people can become gradually acclimatized, Markham in *Climate and the Energy of Nations* [5.2] considers that acclimatization to hot humid weather is achieved by gradually lowering one's efficiency to that appropriate to the climate. It seems therefore desirable to change the climate as far as is possible by providing air conditioning, particularly for sleeping and for mental work. People from a temperate climate invariably heat their houses in cold climates rather than adapt themselves to living in a more spacious version of the igloo.

A few physiological investigations on human tolerance to

high temperatures go back to the 18th century, e.g. in 1775 Blagden demonstrated that a man could survive a dry bulb temperature of 260° F. for eight minutes [5.3].

On the other hand, A. L. Lavoisier, the discoverer of oxygen and carbon dioxide, expressed the view that the malaise experienced in crowded rooms was due to carbon dioxide rather than heat, and throughout the 19th century various toxic substances were examined [5.4]. The anthropotoxin theory was proved false by Halldane in 1905 [5.5], when he established temperature, humidity and air movement as the principal criteria for comfort.

Attention was focussed on the problem by reports of two departmental committees of the British Home Office on Ventilation in Factories (1907) and on Humidity and Ventilation in Cotton Weaving Sheds (1909), which suggested overheating as the principal problem.

A number of instruments have been devised to measure comfort conditions in rooms by physical means. The simplest of these is the katathermometer, suggested by Sir Leonard Hill in 1915; it is a thermometer with a large bulb, and the time required for it to fall through five degrees at body temperature (about 98° F.) is observed to ascertain the cooling power of the air. The most elaborate of the physical devices is Dufton's eupatheoscope [5.6]. The problem appears, however, to be too complex for a physical analogue, and tests on a representative sample of people have proved to be the only satisfactory method. On the basis of such experiments Professor C. P. Yaglou developed the concept of Effective Temperature; this is the temperature of still air saturated with water vapour which gives to a group of people the same subjective comfort sensation as the air in another similar room with a certain temperature, humidity and air movement. The physical measurements of dry-bulb temperature, wet-bulb temperature and air speed are thus reduced to a single numerical criterion. With minor modifications this method has been used in the *Heating, Ventilating, Air-Conditioning Guide* of the American Society of Heating and Air Conditioning Engineers, which is widely accepted as a design standard.

Difference of opinion persists on the significance of humidity for comfort in hot climates. In Australia, for example, Professor W. V. Macfarlane considers that dry bulb temperature is the main criterion [5.7], and this conclusion has been accepted by the Commonwealth Experimental Building Station. The Chief Mechanical Engineer of the Commonwealth Department of Works, on the other hand, assigns much greater importance to the effect of humidity which is included in the concept of Effective Temperature [5.8].

The issue is of considerable importance, because in many instances cooling without lowering the moisture content of the air can be achieved at relatively little cost, e.g. by insulation, by evaporative cooling, and more recently by radiant cooling operated by solar energy [5.9]. Lowering of the moisture content can at present be achieved economically only by refrigeration and by the sealing of all inlets.

To some extent the different comfort indexes proposed reflect different concepts of comfort. The upper limit of the thermal conditions which enable people to perform a task is not the same as the conditions under which it is performed with the greatest competence [5.10].

5.3. Heating, Ventilation and Air Conditioning

Improvement of a cold environment by heating is a relatively simple matter, and it is as old as the use of fire by primitive man. Fixed fireplaces have been found in houses in Troy, dating from about 2,000 B.C., and in other contemporary settlements. These consisted simply of open fires in the centre of the room, with a smoke escape through a hole in the roof. This method was still used in the houses of the English nobility up to the 15th century A.D. Chimneys appear to have been introduced in Italy in the 14th century A.D., and grates in England in the 16th century (previously the fuel was placed in a heap on the floor).

The Greeks and the Romans made use of charcoal braziers for heating, and these were often elaborately decorated objects of bronze, given as presents. In the colder climate of Germany and Holland stoves came to be used from the 16th century. The earliest which survive are made of metal, and it is a matter of opinion whether they are large braziers or enclosed fireplaces. Reports of tile stoves also go back to the 16th century (Fig. 5.3).

The most advanced heating system of the Ancient World was the Roman hypocaust (i.e. "burning underneath") which originated in the 1st century B.C., and subsequently became standard equip-

Fig. 5.3. Swedish tile stove from the 17th century. (From Billington, *A Historical Review of the Art of Heating and Ventilating* [B55].)

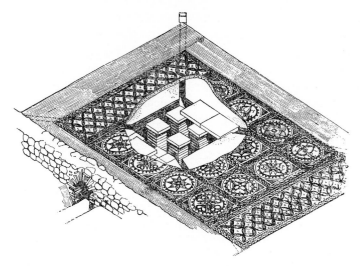

Fig. 5.4. Arrangement of the hypocaust heating beneath a mosaic floor of the Roman city of Verulamium, now St. Albans. (From Davey, *A History of Building Materials* [B20].)

ment in Roman baths and in many villas (Fig. 5.4). A timber or charcoal fire was lit in a stokehole at one end, and the hot gases passed to a chamber beneath the floor, usually placed centrally. The floor was supported on piers, about two feet high, which supported slabs about two feet square. A concrete floor was laid above these, and finally a tile or mosaic finish. The piers were usually made of clay tiles, about eight inches square, bedded in clay which became very hard after exposure to the heat. Numerous examples survive all over Roman England, the best-known being at Aquae Sulis (Bath). In spite of the excellence of the system for a Northern climate and the ease with which it could be built, the concept of the hypocaust did not survive the Roman withdrawal from Britain [B20].

Modern methods of heating date from the Industrial Revolution. William Strutt used gravity warm air heating in Derby Hospital in 1792, and a little later Joseph Bramah used hot-water radiators in Westminster Hospital. Steam-heating is actually the oldest method, since James Watt employed it to heat his office in 1784. Watt and Boulton subsequently installed steam-heating in several factories along with the other plant [B55].

The fan was devised by Dr. Desaguliers in 1734 for improving the ventilation of the British Houses of Parliament. The original model consisted of a paddle wheel, 7 feet in diameter with 1 foot wide radial blades, rotating in a concentric casing, and remained in use for about eighty years [B55].

There are reports of Roman emperors and oriental potentates cooling their chambers by surrounding them with snow or ice; otherwise the earliest suggestion for artificial cooling appears to have come from Dr. D. B. Reid, who was appointed to advise Sir Charles Barry on heating and ventilation during the rebuilding of the British Houses of Parliament (1840–1852). He proposed circulating cool water through the steam-heating pipes during summer; but due to a disagreement with Barry this was not done.

To achieve satisfactory results, mechanical refrigeration is needed. Although the principle had been expounded in a paper published by N. L. S. Carnot in 1824, economical methods became available only at the end of the century. It then became rapidly apparent that air would have to be dehumidified for successful conditioning. Willis Carrier developed the dew-point control system and used it in a New York paper mill in 1902.

While chimneys have been the most prominent feature on the skyline of many houses for centuries, air conditioning may become a more significant factor in architectural design. For reasonably economical operation the outside walls of the building must be sealed and insulated, and windows screened as far as possible from solar radiation.

5.4. *Water Supply and Sanitation*

The Ancient World achieved a remarkably high standard in sanitation which unfortunately was lost with the fall of the Roman Empire, and not achieved again until the 19th century. There are isolated instances of piped water supply and of excellent sanitary installations at a very early age. A latrine has been found in the palace of Sargon II of Assyria (8th century B.C.), with a jar of water beside each seat for flushing. In the palace of Knossos in Crete the latrine was built over a channel with constantly running water [B11].

The outstanding development, however, was in Rome, where the water supply was of a very high quality [5.12]. The Romans had no means of purifying water, but they obtained it from a clean source, and protected it in transit. The water from the different aqueducts was kept entirely separate, and those noted for their purity were reserved for drinking. The eleven ancient aqueducts of Rome had a total length of about three hundred and fifty miles, approximately three hundred miles underground and fifty miles on arches (Fig. 5.5). In Roman Britain there were also a number of aqueducts, at least one, supplying a fort on the Roman Wall in the North, with a length of six miles.

Fig. 5.5.   A reconstruction of the Roman aqueducts at the crossing of the Via Latina. The three water conduits contain the Aquae Marcia, Tepula and Julia, and the other two are the Aquae Claudia and Anio Novis. (From a painting *Wasserleitungen im alten Rom*, by Zeno Diemer, in the Deutsches Museum, Munich.)

In London water was generally obtained from rivers, or pumped from the ground, and pollution was a constant source of trouble. In 1831 alone, 50,000 lives were lost by cholera. When the Lambeth Water Company accepted a recommendation by Dr. John Snow and moved its water intake above the highest point of sewerage discharge into the Thames, a drastic reduction in the incidence of cholera resulted [B12].

In New York the impetus for a proper water supply came from a serious fire in 1835, when five hundred and thirty buildings were destroyed in one night because the existing system proved totally inadequate. The Croton Aquaduct, which brought water from forty miles into the city, was opened in 1842 [B54]. By the turn of the century the Roman achievement had been overshadowed by the British pipelines bringing water from Wales to Liverpool (1881) and Birmingham (1893), and from the Lake District to Manchester (1885).

The sanitary facilities of Imperial Rome also were not surpassed until the late 19th century. The main sewer, the Cloaca Maxima, was started in the 5th century B.C. Eventually most of the *insulae*, or tenements, had water closets on the ground floor. In addition there were numerous public latrines, or *foricae*, for which a small charge was made: –

"The Roman *forica* was public in the full sense of the term. . . . People met there, conversed and exchanged invitations to dinner without embarrassment. And at the same time it was equipped with superfluities which we forgo and decorated with a lavishness we are not wont to spend on such a spot. All round the semicircle or rectangle which it formed, water flowed continuously in little channels, in front of which a score of seats were fixid. The seats were of marble, and the opening was framed by sculptured brackets in the form of dolphins . . . Above the seats it was not unusual to see niches containing statues of gods or heroes . . . or an altar to Fortune; . . . and not infrequently the room was cheered by the sound of a playing fountain." (J. Carcopino, *Daily Life in Ancient Rome*, Penguin Books, London 1956, p. 49.)

Apparently, however, some nightsoil was also thrown from

windows into the street, a practice which persisted right through the Middle Ages into modern times. In 1395 the practice was forbidden in Paris, but it continued in most other cities for centuries longer. In London, Edwin Chadwick in a report on "The Sanitary Conditions of the Labouring Classes" described the sanitary arrangements of the Colosseum in Rome and at the amphitheatre in Verona, and it would seem that these were superior to the facilities in London at the time. He recommended the prompt removal of all refuse from houses and streets, and the disposal of sewerage by underground drains. The London Main Drainage Scheme was built between 1859 and 1867 [B12].

There have been no major changes since that time. We still have to plan our kitchens and sanitary facilities to allow for the fact that drains operate by gravity and must be aligned accordingly, and we still have to provide for the removal of solid refuse in garbage containers and provide for their removal and collection. Although mechanical systems of garbage disposal have been used occasionally in blocks of flats, they have not been widely adopted because of their cost, and the need to separate soft refuse from tins etc.

Sanitary fittings for kitchens and bathrooms, however, are still in the process of evolution, and this is one of the major causes for houses being considered obsolescent when the fabric is still in perfect condition.

The first water closet was developed by Joseph Bramah in England in 1788; a similar type is still used today in railway carriages. In 1833 the first pan closet was manufactured in England; it had a water seal and was much cheaper than Bramah's valve closet [B1]. About 1890 the earthenware washdown water closet, still used today, appeared in the United States [B54].

While the Romans treated bathing as a social occasion and the bath occupied a large space, the medieval bathtub was very small because it had to be filled and emptied by hand. In the first half of the 19th century pressurized water supply and sanitary drains became more common, and bathtubs became larger. Occasionally shower fittings were used above the tub. About 1870 the white-enamelled cast-iron bathtub made its appearance, at first free-standing on iron legs, now commonly built-in.

One-piece sink and drainboard combination fixtures with integral splashback were introduced ca. 1920, and two-compartment sinks in one piece ca. 1930. Stainless steel began to be used ca. 1950. Washing machines are probably still in the process of evolution.

5.5. *The Significance of Electricity for the Design of Dwellings*

The use of electricity in buildings is similarly a very recent development. The article on Electricity in the Ninth Edition of the Encyclopaedia Britannica, published in 1879, runs to over 100 pages; however, most of the significant practical applications have developed since then. The electrical generator was discovered by Michael Faraday in England in 1831; but power generation as a major enterprise was mainly an American development, pioneered by George Westinghouse and Thomas Alva Edison in the eighteen-eighties. The electric light bulb was first demonstrated by Joseph Wilson Swan in 1878, and Edison, working independently, patented his lamp in 1879. In 1876 Alexander Graham Bell patented the telephone. The first successful electric lift was installed by Otis Brothers in the Demarest Building, New York, in 1889. All these innovations came from the United States.

The effect of the electrification of the services on the design of buildings has been tremendous. It cannot be said that high-rise buildings would be impossible without electricity, whereas they could not be operated without piped sewage, lifts, artificial light and mechanical ventilation. The lifts could be hydraulic, the lighting by gas, the ventilation supplied by steam power, and internal communication could be by pneumatic tube. However, the ease with which electricity can be supplied through small ducts, without concern for sharp corners or loss of gravity head, and the precise controls made possible through its use, have largely contributed to the present freedom of interior planning and the high quality of the building services. In factories, machines with individual electric motors have obviated the need for overhead shafting, which had been a major limitation to the layout of the production process.

The most important post-war contribution has been in the field of automation. The automatic internal telephone, with automatic connection to the external system, and the electronic supervisory system for lifts require only maintenance and supervisory staff.

5.6. *Vertical Transportation, Internal Communications, and Security Devices*

Mechanical hoisting devices had been used by the Romans, and they featured prominently in the writings of Renaissance authors on mechanics (*see* Section 1.4). Hoists were already familiar in mines in the late 18th century, when mechanical power came to be used for their operation. Numerous fatal accidents occurred when the cage dropped to the bottom through failure of the ropes or the hoisting device. The invention of Elisha Graves Otis consisted of a safety device to prevent the car from falling. In 1854 he demonstrated it publicly at the Crystal Palace Exhibition in New York. He had himself hoisted to the ceiling and then ordered the rope to be cut; this released the safety catch to engage ratchets in the guide rails (Fig. 5.6).

The idea did not immediately catch on. Safety lifts were used for goods, but a passenger lift was installed in New York only in 1857, belt-driven at a speed of forty feet per minute. Hydraulic lifts followed in 1878 (Fig. 5.7), and by the turn of the century they reached speeds of up to seven hundred feet per minute. This is still regarded as a reasonable operating speed for medium-sized buildings, and it focussed attention on the problem of control. Seven hundred feet per minute being equal to eight miles per hour, then the speed limit for cyclists in New York streets, the unaided operator had difficulty in controlling it. The first electric lift was installed in 1889, and Ward Leonard multivoltage control was added in 1892. The first push-button control was used in the Vanderbilt residence in 1893, and gearless traction followed at the turn of the century.

The immediate effect of the passenger lift was a change of values. Top floors had commanded low rentals because of the stairs, and were usually allocated to the janitor. They now became the most desirable accommodation, and the height of city buildings increased above the usual four to five storeys. In 1879 the Boreel Building was designed around a group of high-speed lifts, and the lift lobby became the central feature of the entrance (Fig. 5.7). In 1882 the Montauk Building, the original skyscraper [B23], in Chicago rose to ten storeys on load-bearing walls, and space in the basement was so restricted that the boilers and engines for the two hydraulic lifts had to be placed in an outdoor court behind the shafts.

Fig. 5.6.   First public demonstration of the safety lift, New York 1854.

The Monadnock Building, designed by Burnham and Root in Chicago in 1889, was the highest building with load-bearing walls. It has sixteen floors, and required a wall thickness of six feet at the base [B24]. The skeleton iron frame, first used by W. L. B. Jenney in the ten-storey Home Insurance Building in Chicago in 1885 (*see* Section 2.2) removed the limitation on height, and allowed

Fig. 5.7. High-speed hydraulic lift in the Boreel Building, New York 1879.

more space in the basement for services. In the next fifty years the height of buildings increased rapidly, culminating with the one-hundred-and-two-storey Empire State Building in 1931, and it became evident that even with high-speed lifts there was an economical limit.

Lifts also began to be used as aids in construction. Thus the passenger lift inside the Washington Monument, Washington's five-hundred-and-fifty-five feet stone obelisk, was originally installed for construction in 1880.

Some of the internal communication methods developed in the 19th century are now obsolete. The sliding wire system, used for taking money to the central cash register in stores, has probably been superseded largely because the modern cash register allows a better check on the money handled; an obstacle to the planning of interiors has thus been removed. Pneumatic tubes still have some use; but with the increasing use of internal telephones since the nineties, and the recent adaptation of closed-circuit television for checking records, the need for physically transporting pieces of paper has been greatly reduced.

The oldest of the fire safety devices is the automatic sprinkler. Perforated water pipes which could be turned on from outside date from ca. 1850. Sprinklers hand-operated from outside valves followed in the next decade. Because of the damage caused by the water, the idea of an automatic sprinkler head which responded to local rise in temperature received much attention, and Frederick Grinell patented the first device in America in 1882; it depended on the expansion of a liquid in a glass tube, and the principle is still used today.

5.7. Sun Control

The basic theory of sun control was well-known to the Alexandrian mathematicians in the second century A.D., and Book III of Ptolemy's *Almagest* is devoted to the motion of the sun. While there are references to the sunlight penetration into buildings in the 18th and 19th century, systematic interest in the subject dates from this century. The three contributing factors were the freedom of design afforded by the abandonment of eclectic façades, the attention given to the beneficial effects of sunlight in Northern Europe, and the problems of overheating produced by the use of larger areas of glass, particularly in Southern Europe and South America. In the post-war years the realization of the inter-relation between sun control and the cost of air-conditioning has been the most significant factor in encouraging simpler and more precise design methods.

(a)

Although sunlight penetration can be worked out by trigonometry, it is a time-consuming matter when a number of alternative designs are considered, and many architects find the calculations beyond their competence. Graphical methods and models have therefore become popular. There are several different types of sun machine (Fig. 5.8).

The heliodon built at the British Building Research Station by A. F. Dufton and H. E. Beckett was described in the *Journal of Scientific Instruments* in 1932 (Vol. 9, p. 251), but the active use of

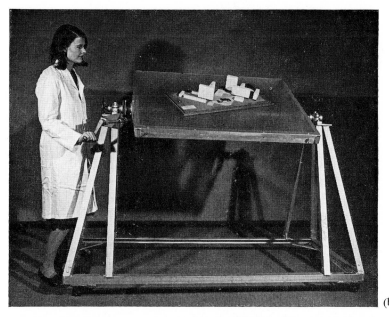

(b)

Fig. 5.8. (a) The Solarscope of the University of Sydney. The model is placed on the platform, and the light representing the sun is moved to imitate the latitude, the time of the day, and the time of the year. The accuracy of the device is limited by the practicable length of the rod which limits the distance of the light from the model. (b) The Heliodon of the University of Sydney. The model is placed on the transparent table, which is rotated in accordance with the azimuth and the altitude of the sun, calculated from the latitude, the time of the day, and the time of the year. The horizontal light source is placed as far away as possible to imitate parallel sunlight. The device is more accurate, but not direct-reading.

sun-control models by architects dates only from the forties. For the design of normal buildings and groups of buildings, simplified devices, like the "Little Sundial" devised by Gunnar Pleijel in Sweden, have proved adequate. It consists of a three inch sundial (without correction for the equation of time) for the appropriate latitude; this is placed on a small model, which is then rotated to show the shadows at any required time. The problem can also be solved on the drawing board by graphical solutions for the trigono-metric equations. These were proposed by H. B. Molesworth (*"Obstruction to Sunlight"*, E. and F. N. Spon, London, 1902) and later modified by P. J. Waldram (*R.I.B.A. Journal*, Vol. 40, 1933, p. 51) and others.

The problem of sunlight control has two aspects. In the colder climates it is important to admit adequate light, and the screening effect of surrounding tall buildings is of particular importance. For the study of this aspect Pleijel developed the Globoscope [5.13]; this consists of a paraboloidal mirror, in which a distorted image of the surrounding buildings is seen in stereographic projection, as observed from above. The sunlight penetration is studied by superimposing a transparent sun-path diagram.

In regions near the equator exclusion of excessive heat is the principal problem, although summer heat loads due to solar radiation can be serious even in Scandinavia. From the sunlight penetration diagrams the amount of solar radiation can be computed [5.13]. As the sun is at a high altitude when its heat should be excluded, and at a low altitude in winter when sunlight indoors is pleasant, the technical aspect of screening undesirable sunlight is relatively simple. Aesthetically, however, it presents a difficult problem, because a screening device can become the most promi-nent object of the façade.

Traditional architectural styles did not necessarily exclude sun-screening. For example, the adaptation of Greek Revival architecture to the conditions of the Southern United States resulted in the wide verandahs which still survive in the Garden District of New Orleans. However, the verandahs of these houses, as those of the colonial architecture of Australia, were not scientifically designed and their width excluded sunlight altogether to give a dark, and in winter a cold, interior.

Modern sunshading devices aim to exclude the sun only when it is not wanted. One of the earliest examples is the Ministry of Education in Rio de Janeiro, designed in the thirties by a committee of which Lucio Costa and Oscar Niemeyer were members, with Le Corbusier as consultant; it featured integral adjustable louvres [B4]. Although adjustable devices give full sun control with the least trouble, arbitrary adjustment by the occupants gives the building a patchy appearance. Even with fixed devices it is difficult to achieve a satisfactory façade composed almost entirely of louvres, whether vertical or horizontal. The obstruction of the view is another problem in high-rise buildings, where the views are often an important amenity. Balconies of suitable width can provide the necessary control; a horizontal screen of slanted louvres allows even closer design limits [B47].

5.8. Natural Lighting

The systematic design of the daylighting of buildings is also a development of this century. In Great Britain a right of free access of daylight to the windows of a building is acquired either by a grant or by uninterrupted enjoyment for a period of twenty years. Until 1922 there was no definition of this legal right; but in that year a judge adopted a daylight factor of 0.2 as the border line between adequacy and inadequacy of the daylight in a room. The daylight factor, which is defined as the ratio of the illumination on a horizontal plane inside to the simultaneous exterior illumination, has therefore acquired specific significance in England, which may account for the preference shown for the daylight factor as a design tool [B48]. Because of its geometric basis the design can easily be adapted to protractors and graphic constructions [5.14]. In America the lumen method, proposed by Harrison and Anderson, has been preferred for both natural and artificial lighting [5.15].

Both the calculating aids based on the daylight factor and the tables produced by Professor J. W. Griffith, based on the lumen method [5.16] make a number of simplifying assumptions, and model studies in artificial skies are used for the more complex problems. The *Commission Internationale de l'Eclairage* has adopted the proposal made by Professor Moon and Mrs. Spencer in 1942 (*Illuminating Engineering*, Vol. 37, p. 707) for a standard of the overcast condition normally considered in design

$$L_\theta = \tfrac{1}{3} L_z (1 + 2 \cos \theta)$$

(where L_θ and L_z are the luminances at an angle θ above the horizon and at the zenith respectively) and artificial skies are designed to give this distribution of luminance for model studies.

5.9. Artificial Lighting

While daylight has always been with us, but cannot be properly controlled, good artificial lighting can be designed by the architect or his illuminating engineer. The discovery of the electric light bulb was therefore of the greatest importance to architectural design.

The earliest lamps found by archaeologists date from about 2,500 B.C. Vegetable or fish oil, and candles made from tallow, an edible fat, remained the principal sources of artificial light until the 18th century; beeswax was never available in large quantities. Most of these fuels were edible, so that in times of food shortage there was a tendency to economize on light [B50]. In the 18th century the new sperm whale fisheries supplemented the supplies of wax and tallow, and vast chandeliers with numerous candles became common among the well-to-do. Candlemaking became mechanized by the invention of machines which do not differ greatly from those still in use today. Several new types of vegetable and mineral oil were discovered for use in lamps, and coal gas was used for the first time in Whitehaven, England, in 1765.

In 1810 the Gas Light and Coke Company was formed in London, but the light obtained from gas flames was not much better than candle or oil light until Welsbach invented in 1885 an incandescent mantle composed of cotton impregnated with thorium and cerium oxide. In the meantime fuel for oil lamps became cheaper and more reliable when W. E. Binney started its manufacture from petroleum deposits in Derbyshire in 1847; this was followed by the discovery of large reserves in Austria in 1853 and in Pennsylvania in 1859 [B1].

Oil and gas lighting were therefore well established industries when Swan and Edison, working independently, invented the electric light bulb in 1878–1879. The carbon filaments gave way about 1897 to incandescent oxides like those used in gas mantles, and to coiled tungsten filaments in argon-filled bulbs about 1913 [B50].

The first demonstration of the glow from an electric discharge in a vacuum was given before the Royal Society in 1710, but the first practical discharge lamps were only made at the turn of the century. Claude began to make neon display tubes in France from 1910, and these rapidly became the most prominent feature of city streets at night. The proper relation of illuminated advertising to the general design of buildings has hardly been explored, and a great opportunity is being lost through our failure to include the appearance of the advertising signs in the initial architectural design. In interior lighting, discharge and fluorescent tubes have become increasingly important since the nineteen-forties because of their low power consumption.

The cost of electricity in relation to other commodities has steadily fallen, and illumination levels have increased accordingly. Recent studies have concentrated on the quality of lighting, the correct placement of the fittings and the avoidance of glare.

The versatile nature of modern light fittings has made it much easier to use light as a major aesthetic element in the design of buildings, perhaps for the first time since the Gothic invention of large stained glass windows (*see* Section 6.3). As a form of architectural expression, lighting can be used to emphasize the architectural form, a specific surface, or a sculptural effect. The light fittings themselves may be prominent visual objects, or they can be subordinate or disappear entirely from view. So far the technical possibilities have perhaps tempted us to use too much light with too little effect [5.17].

5.10. Acoustics

Of all branches of architectural science, acoustics is the one in which the scientific understanding of the Classical World had furthest advanced by comparison with our present knowledge of this subject. Vitruvius discusses the subject in considerable detail: –

"Voice is a flowing breath of air, perceptible to the hearing by contact. It moves in an endless number of circular rounds, like the innumerably increasing circular waves which appear when a stone is thrown into smooth water, and which keeps on spreading indefinitely from the centre unless interrupted by narrow limits, or by some obstruction which prevents such waves from reaching their end in due formation. When they are interrupted by obstructions, the first waves, flowing back, break up the formation of those which follow.

In the same manner the voice executes its movements in concentric circles; but while in the case of water the circles move horizontally on a plane surface, the voice not only proceeds horizontally, but also ascends vertically by regular stages. Therefore, as in the case of the waves formed in the water, so it is in the case of the voice: the first wave, when there is no obstruction to interrupt it, does not break up the second or the following waves, but they all reach the ears of the lowest and the highest spectators without an echo.

Hence the ancient architects, following in the footsteps of nature, perfected the ascending rows of seats in theatres from their investigations of the ascending voice, and, by means of the canonical theory of the mathematicians and that of the musicians, endeavoured to make every voice uttered on the stage come with greater clearness and sweetness to the ears of the audience. For just as musical instruments are brought to perfection of clearness in the sound of their strings by means of bronze plates or horn *echeia*, so the ancients devised methods of increasing the power of the voice in theatres through the application of harmonics." (*Ten Books of Architecture* [B5], pp. 138–9).

Vitruvius then proceeds to explain how the voice can be reinforced by placing sounding vessels in niches. None have survived, but presumably the actors were trained to intone their lines at the natural frequency of these resonators. However, this was not the only method used to obtain resonance: –

"Somebody will perhaps say that many theatres are built every year in Rome, and that in them no attention at all is paid to these principles; but he will be in error, from the fact that all our public theatres made of wood contain a great deal of boarding, which must be resonant. This may be observed from the behaviour of those who sing to the lyre, who, when they wish to sing in a higher key, turn towards the folding doors on the stage, and thus by their aid are reinforced with a sound in harmony with their voice. But when theatres are built of solid materials, like masonry, stone or marble, which cannot be resonant, then the principles of the *echeia* must be applied." (p. 145).

Vitruvius then proceeds to lay down in some detail the geometric proportions of the ideal Roman theatre, which give the plan and elevation shown in Fig. 5.9.

The Greeks and the Romans used open-air theatres. By modern standards they were very large. The Dionysian theatre in Athens, excavated in 1862 [B1], is estimated to have seated thirty thousand people, and the largest Roman theatres are reported by Pliny to have held up to eighty thousand. (The Royal Albert Hall in London, one of the modern world's largest concert halls, accommodates six thousand people, including one thousand standees [B52]; it should be noted that sporting arenas are excluded from this discussion.) It would have been impracticable even for Roman architects to erect satisfactory roof structures and provide for adequate ventilation. An essential feature of these huge open-air theatres is the high wall at the back of the stage which acts both as a sound insulator against outside noises, and as a reflector for the stage. The "orchestra", the flat space in front of the stage platform, is also acoustically important.

These features were still maintained in the Elizabethan theatre of the 16th century which, while providing a roof over the stage and over the more important members of the audience, was open

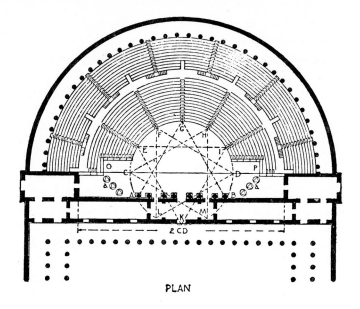

PLAN

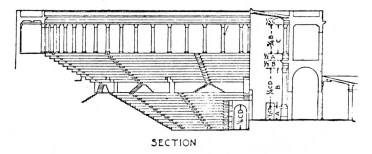

SECTION

Fig. 5.9.   The Roman Theatre according to Vitruvius [B5].

to the sky and had a tall stage tower as reflector behind the stage. The size of the auditorium, however, was more like that of a modern theatre than the Roman prototype.

Although some Gothic cathedrals have remarkably fine acoustics for organ and choral music, the scientific interest in acoustics revived only with the Renaissance. In 1650 Athanasius Kircher, better known as the discoverer of the magic lantern, discussed in *Musurgia Universalis* the problem of the sound mirror [B51] and the associated problem of the whispering gallery, which can be found in a number of Renaissance buildings, not always created intentionally.

The speed of sound was measured by Martin Mersenne in the early 17th century as 1,380 feet per second, an error of only 27%. Galileo mentions the laws of vibrations in his *Discorsi*, [2.1], and Otto von Guericke demonstrated in 1672 that sound, unlike light, cannot travel in a vacuum [B7].

From the 18th century onward composers and musicians also became interested in the subject. The violonist Guiseppe Tartini and the composer Jean-Phillipe Rameau were both interested in harmonics, and the reason for the frequency intervals between them.

A good deal of the acoustic knowledge transmitted from classical times has, however, given rise to misconceptions that still linger with many musicians and concert-goers. Beranek [B52] mentions the belief that broken wine-bottles beneath the stage are good for acoustics. It is true that some of the best concert halls have broken bottles under the stage, thrown there by the builders, but so have some of the worst. Vitruvius' sounding vessels certainly were not like this. Beranek also gives no credence to the idea that a wooden interior is essential, based on the concept of the wooden violin, and perhaps on Vitruvius' ideas copied by writers throughout the Renaissance; he considers on the contrary that hard plaster, masonry or thick wood are necessary to conserve energy.

Although a number of engineers and physicists took an interest in architectural acoustics, the real beginning of the scientific study of the subject are the experiments on reverberation time, absorption and the formation of echoes, carried out by Professor W. C. Sabine at Harvard University in the early years of this century [5.18]. The scientific study of acoustics developed rapidly thereafter, with contributors too numerous to mention. It is now possible to design scientifically auditoria for speech and to avoid the worst mistakes in concert halls and opera houses. However, the perfect auditorium for music is still a matter of judgement and luck; the detailed acoustical studies made prior to the design of the Royal Festival Hall in London and Philharmonic Hall of the Lincoln Centre in New York have only produced good, not great, concert halls [B52].

5.11. Noise Control

While noise control is a branch of architectural acoustics, it received little attention before the 20th century. City streets in Imperial Rome and in some medieval cities were probably quite noisy; but the problem became acute only with the invention of motor cars, high speed machinery, and particularly aeroplanes. Moreover traditional buildings for the upper classes were designed with thick walls, usually of stone or brick, so that the mass acted as an effective sound barrier. In modern lightweight construction sound insulation is one of the most difficult problems, and the standard expected by people in the middle and working classes is rising with higher standards of living.

The Acoustical Materials Association, founded in 1933, started issuing bulletins on sound-absorption coefficients in 1934, and a number of papers appeared in the thirties, partly motivated by the problems created by aeroplanes, then still relatively new. The mass-law, which gives a linear relation between sound insulation in decibels and the logarithm of the weight of the partition per unit area, was proved after the construction of the first acoustic transmission chamber at Geneva, Illinois, now the Riverbank Acoustical Laboratories of the Illinois Institute of Technology.

During the Second World War, Dr. S. S. Stevens investigated the psychological aspects of noise control and speech communication posed by tanks, military aircraft etc. at the Harvard psycho-acoustic laboratory, and Dr. L. L. Beranek, also at Harvard, developed structures and materials which were light in weight for a given noise reduction.

In the post-war years the British Building Research Station has made extensive field measurements of sound insulation between dwellings, culminating in 1960 in Research Paper No. 33, which contains data sheets on four hundred and sixty-four forms of construction. The problem remains, however, one of the most difficult in architectural science, because the sound insulation of a new form of construction cannot be fully predicted from theoretical considerations, because noise levels are still increasing in spite of measures to reduce noise at the source, and because the current trend towards lightness and mobility of partitions runs counter to the mass-law of insulation [B53].

5.12. The Integrated Design of Building Services

The growing complexity of the services and of the functional problems of the building envelope raises problems of integration which have only recently been given serious attention. In traditional construction the chimney always formed part of the architect's design, and drains had to be installed during construction; however, electric conduits, water and gas pipes were not always located during design, and holes were frequently cut for them in the completed fabric of the building and then made good.

This is not feasible with many modern materials and dry methods of construction, where both the cutting and the making good are more difficult. Furthermore the greatly increased number of locations for electric light and power, and the large volume occupied by air conditioning ducts makes integrated planning of the services during the initial stages of the architectural design very desirable. One of the arguments in favour of modular coordination and industrialized building methods is the greater measure of control possible in standardized sub-assemblies.

The functional efficiency of the fabric of the building also must be considered in the design of the building services. The shielding of the walls and windows from the sun effects both the lighting and the heating or cooling of the building. Ventilation, both through windows and through ducts, affects noise control, as does the design of the partitions (particularly if they are movable), of the outside walls, and of the ceiling containing the services.

This is a task of immense complexity which makes great demands on the architects and the consulting engineers, and it may reasonably be asked why we have abandoned solid masonry buildings. These gave generally good sound insulation, and in temperate climates provided an adequate thermal capacity to produce satisfactory indoor conditions in all but the hottest weather without artificial cooling. At least part of the answer lies in the need to build high when cities are constantly growing more populous.

The limit of the load bearing wall was reached when, in 1889 the Monadnock Building was started in Chicago on solid load-bearing walls seventy-two inches thick, to reach a height of sixteen floors [B24]. With a curtain wall this can be reduced to three or four inches, irrespective of height.

Vertical transportation, and electrical services and communication systems are the inevitable by-product of high-density living. Air-conditioning may not be strictly necessary in many large cities; but the experience of Sydney, at any rate, shows that a luxury can quickly become a necessity when the technique has been mastered. In 1950 rentable air-conditioned offices were non-existent; by 1964 only air-conditioned offices were built for tenancies in new City buildings, because no property owner in the City expected to be able to let offices without air-conditioning at an economical rental.

When the load-bearing steel frame, the lift installation and the air-conditioning plant are all factory produced, it becomes pertinent to ask whether the production of the components of the entire high-rise building, and indeed of any building, could be transferred to the factory.

Chapter 6

The New Building Materials
and the Industrialization of Building

The method employed I would gladly explain
While I have it so clear in my head,
If I had but the time and you had but the brain—
But much yet remains to be said.

Lewis Carroll [6.19]

6.1. Statistics and Quality Control

Quality control over traditional materials was exercised largely by observation of long-term performances. Size, which is a critical factor in metallic units and in precast concrete, barely mattered in bricks where changes in dimensions could be taken up in the joint, and natural stone and timber were generally trimmed to their final dimensions on the site. Strength could not be tested readily before the invention of testing machines in the 18th century (*see* Section 1.5); but only traditional timber structures depended on strength for their stability, and these were often grossly over-designed.

The main problem of the classical use of materials was their durability. This was controlled by using reliable sources of material; sometimes materials were exposed to the weather for a year to detect obviously defective pieces. These practices were well established in the 1st century B.C.:

"There are also several quarries called Anician in the territory of Tarquinii, the stone being of the colour of peperino. The principal workshops lie round the lake of Bolsena and in the prefecture of Statonia. This stone has innumerable good qualities. Neither the season of frost nor exposure to fire can harm it, but it remains solid and lasts to a great age, because there is only a little air and fire in its natural composition, a moderate amount of moisture, and a great deal of the earth*. Hence its structure is of close texture and solid, and so it cannot be injured by the weather or by the force of fire.

This may best be seen from monuments in the neighbourhood of the town of Ferento which are made of stone from these quarries . . . Old as these are, they look as fresh as if they were only just finished . . . If the quarries were only near Rome, all our buildings might well be constructed from the products of these workshops.

But since, on account of the proximity of the stone quarries of Grotta Rossa, Palla, and the others that are nearest to the city, necessity drives us to make use of their products, we must proceed as follows, if we wish our work to be finished without flaws. Let the stone be taken from the quarry two years before building is to begin, and not in winter but in summer. Then let it lie exposed in an open place. Such stone as has been damaged by two years of exposure should be used in the foundations. The rest, which remains unhurt, has passed the test of nature and will endure in those parts of the building which are above ground. This precaution should be observed not only with dimension stone, but also with the rubble which is used in the walls." (From Vitruvius' *Ten Books of Architecture* [B5], p. 50.)

With the advent of modern structural engineering, based on the strength of materials, rather than the balancing of heavy masses, quality control became more important, and the regular testing of materials became a common practice in the 19th century. It was then observed that tests on apparently similar pieces of material yielded widely differing results. Assuming that the strength of a structure depends on the strength of its weakest part, the strength of the weakest test piece acquires special significance. Without testing every piece of material, and thus destroying the material and leaving none for use in the building, we cannot be

---

* Vitruvius' reference is to the four elements of Aristotle, which dominated the ideas of the Ancient World, the Middle Ages and the Renaissance on the structure of materials. The scientific study of chemistry dates from the late 18th century.

sure that we know the minimum strength. On the other hand, it is unlikely that the weakest piece of material will be used in the very few highest-stressed parts of the structure. The strength of the structure can therefore be stated only as a probability, and we must accept the probability of a structure falling down because of defective material, provided it is very low.

The shape of the curve recording the distribution of a large number of experimental data from a few very low results through the average, with the maximum number of results, to a few very high results, was established about 1800, and it is still called after Carl Friedrich Gauss (whose name has also been given to the unit of magnetic measurement) [B9]. The less the spread of the curve, the better the degree of quality control. Once this is known, it is possible to assign an average strength which will ensure that only a

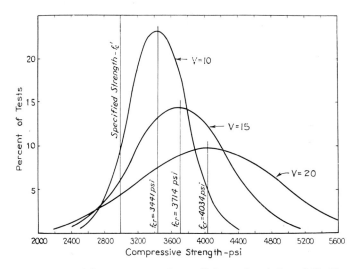

Fig. 6.1. Normal frequency curve for coefficients of variation of 10, 15, and 20%. The required average compressive concrete cylinder strength, f_{cr}, is based on a probability of 1 in 10 that a test will fall below a specified strength, f'_c of 3000 p.s.i. The coefficient of variation is the statistical measure of the degree of dispersion of the experimental data. (From *Recommended Practice for Evaluation of Compression Test Results of Field Concrete*, Standard 214, published by the American Concrete Institute, Detroit, 1957.)

given proportion, say 1 in 10, fall below the acceptable minimum *m*, which determines the probability of failure.

Although quality control had been used by American industry since the early years of this century, statistical factors became a major factor in production control only during the Second World War. In 1940 the American Standards Association initiated a project which led to the publication of the American Defense Emergency Standards. The British Standards Institution adopted these in 1942, and the Standards Association of Australia in 1943.

A statistical method for evaluating compression test-results for concrete was accepted by the American Concrete Institute in 1957, and this resulted in a considerable economy of the most widely used structural material (Fig. 6.1).

6.2. The Nineteenth Century Produces New Metals

No metals were employed in the building industry before the end of the 19th century which had not been known to the Ancient World. Copper and lead were used for roofing, and iron and bronze (an alloy of copper and tin) for cramps, dowels and door hinges about 3,000 years ago. Roman copper and lead water pipes have been found. Bronze was used on both the inside and the outside of the Pantheon's roof in Rome (*see* Section 1.2) in the second century A.D. The gold-plated bronze tiles covering the roof outside were removed to Constantinople by the Emperor Constans II; the bronze girders holding up the portico and the bronze covering the inside of the dome remained until the reign of Pope Urban the VIII in the 17th century, when they were turned into eighty cannon for the Castel Sant'Angelo and Bernini's baldacchino in St. Peter's [B11].

Leone Batista Alberti in 1452 [B6, p. 54] recommends cramps of brass (an alloy of copper and zinc) fixed with lead, particularly for marble because of the danger of staining when iron is used.

After the 12th century iron became the principal metal for building. Its main use was in wrought iron screens, nails and cramps. There were occasional structural applications, e.g. a series of iron ties in the rebuilding of Canterbury Cathedral after its destruction by fire in 1174. In Westminster Abbey the iron ties appear to be part of the original construction, about 1245, and not a later reinforcement [B21]. In the Renaissance iron was used for chains to restrain the hoop tension in domes [B16], e.g. in St. Peter's, Rome, and St. Paul's, London (*see* Section 1.4), and to an increasing extent it was used for machinery and hoisting devices.

The quantity and quality of iron improved gradually, and its cost was reduced drastically after about 1775 [B21], and in the 19th century it became the most important structural material (*see* Section 2.1).

Aluminium is the first of the new metals. Its name derives from alum (a double sulphate of aluminium and a uni-valent metal), the *alumen* used by the Romans for dyeing. Sir Humphrey Davy thought that alumina, the naturally occurring oxide of aluminium, had a metallic base; but the Danish scientist Hans Christian Oersted was the first to separate the metal by electrolysis. In 1845 Friedrich Wöhler in Germany produced enough of the metal to determine its density and physical properties; however, it remained a rarity until Paul Louis Heroult in France, and Charles Martin Hall in America, working independently, in 1886 developed the commercial process still in use today. The Ninth Edition of the Encyclopaedia Britannica, published in 1875, described aluminium as a metal used in jewellery and, because of its light weight, in balance beams. In 1893 aluminium was used for the Eros statue in Piccadilly Circus, London. One of the earliest architectural uses was as an ornamental sheet metal cornice on the Canada Life Insurance Building in Montreal in 1896, and the first corrugated aluminium roof was laid on the Chief Secretary's Office in Macquarie Street, Sydney, in 1900. The sheets had been fixed with copper nails (a mistake frequently made for many years thereafter although the electro-chemical series of metals was well-known at the time), which produced holes in the aluminium; however, the sheets were other-wise in excellent condition when replaced in 1937.

Because of the high chemical reactivity of aluminium, the durability conferred by the hard oxide skin was not appreciated at first, and high price limited use until the thirties. In 1932 cast aluminium spandrels were used in the Rockefeller Center, New York, and in 1936 Sir Giles Scott used aluminium windows and doors for the Cambridge University Library. During the 1939–45 war, world production of aluminium more than doubled, and the building industry absorbed a large part of the surplus after the war.

The experience gained with the production of aeroplanes and the urgent need for housing led to the manufacture of complete metal houses. These houses were not economical at the time and did not meet with much popular approval; neither did the lightness of the aluminium compensate for the high price in purely structural applications. Aluminium windows, however, proved competitive with steel because of the attractive and durable surface, and in the fifties the metal came to be used extensively in curtain walls. Anodized coatings were used from the early thirties. A wide range of colours can be introduced into the oxide skin; organic colours, however, have faded rapidly in sunlight, and only mineral pigments are now employed.

The first prominent architectural use of stainless steel was in the Chrysler Building, New York, whose tower was sheathed in the metal, in 1929. In 1932 the column and mullion covers of the Empire State Building were made from it. The first stainless steel curtain wall was manufactured in 1948 for the General Electric turbine building, Schenectady, a four-storey structure, and in 1951 the entire surface of the twenty-four-storey Gateway Center in Pittsburgh was covered with 22-gauge stainless steel, with relatively small windows.

Copper and Bronze, in addition to their traditional uses, have also been used for covering walls, but only on a limited scale, since aluminium can be anodized to give a similar appearance more cheaply.

6.3. Glass

The origin of glass-making is lost in antiquity. Pliny related how some Phoenician merchants, shipwrecked in Syria, lit a fire on the sandy shore and supported their cooking pots on blocks on carbonate of soda salvaged from their ship; in the morning they discovered glass among the ashes. At any rate, the oldest glass has been found in Syria, and from there it was introduced into Egypt about 1,500 B.C. At first glass was used only for small containers and jewellery. In the first century it came to be used in mosaics and for windows, and it is found in most Roman ruins in Britain [B20]. The earliest windows were cast and had a blue or green tint. Colourless window glass dates from about the fourth century, but it was not really transparent because of the many imperfections, and this probably explains why glass windows were used only rarely in Roman architecture.

The art of making glass survived the fall of the Roman Empire, particularly in Syria, where crown glass made its first appearance in the eighth century.

While coloured glass was known to the Romans, painted glass windows are only beginning to be mentioned in Italian and French manuscripts of the 10th century. The oldest surviving stained glass windows date from the twelfth century [B44]. The Gothic stained glass window had a strong religious significance; but since glass could not at the time be made properly transparent, the stained glass was also aesthetically preferable. The reduction in light through colouring in turn encouraged large windows.

The German monk Theophilus Rogerus in the eleventh or twelfth century described in *De diversis artibus* (translated by Robert Hendrie, Murray, London 1847) the manufacture of cylinder or broad glass, which may have been practised since Roman days. A ball of glass was gathered at the end of a blow iron, blown into a sphere, and by swinging it to and fro it was elongated into a closed cylinder. The ends were then cut off. The cylinder was reheated and cut down its length with shears, and opened out in the furnace (Fig. 6.2). Opinions differ on the date of the introduction of this method into England. It was greatly improved when glass makers arrived from Lorraine in the 16th century, and a large number of technical terms in the glass industry are still of French derivation [B44].

In Elizabethan days the supply of glass thus became more

Fig. 6.2.   Final stage in the manufacture of broad glass. The cylinder of glass has been split longitudinally and is ready to be opened out into a sheet in a gently heated oven [6.1].

generous in England, and windows increased in size, partly due to the greater safety of the times, and partly through the adaptation of the Renaissance style to a more Northerly climate (*see* Section 5.2). As in the Gothic church, window panes were limited to about eight inches square, and assembled with lead into larger units. The assembly was, however, weak, so that stone mullions were used at intervals of about thirty inches.

Crown glass had come to England from Venice and from Normandy since the 14th century, and local manufacture dates from the 17th century. (However, D. B. Harden [6.1] considers that crown glass was made in England in the Middle Ages.) The first recorded use of the balanced sliding sash in England was in 1685, when Inigo Jones' Banqueting House in Whitehall was stripped of its original windows and provided with sashes, glazed with crown glass [B44].

The sash window filled with brilliantly clear, often slightly curved, crown glass, became one of the characteristics of Georgian architecture. Crown glass was made by spinning, which limited its size to about fifty-four inches diameter. It did not come into contact with any other materials during manufacture, so that it had a freedom from defects which cast glass did not acquire until the perfection of sheet glass manufacture by Robert Lucas Chance in 1832. Crown glass dominated English window glazing until the nineteenth century (Fig. 6.3).

In the seventeenth century orangeries for growing subtropical plants began to appear in the great houses. They were at first merely conventional buildings with large windows. In 1795 Humphrey Repton in *Sketches and Hints on Landscape Gardening* suggested glass roofs, and in the early nineteenth century iron frames were used to produce hot houses formed entirely of glass (Fig. 6.4).

The Crystal Palace (*see* Section 6.6) is technically a similar building. It led to the glass-roofed railway station and the glass roofed department store, in which the goods could be easily examined even at a considerable distance from the outside wall. The glass-roofed light court and the shopping arcade remained an

Fig. 6.3. The process of crown-glass making. (From William Cooper's *Crown-Glass Cutter and Glazier's Manual*, 1825; by courtesy of the British Museum.)

Fig. 6.4. Interior of the Conservatory at the Horticultural Gardens in Chiswick, 1841. (From *London*, edited by Charles Knight and published by Knight and Co., London 1842.)

important element in architectural planning until the perfection of artificial lighting in the twentieth century.

In the middle of the nineteenth century the manufacture of plate glass improved to the extent that large sheets became possible, and the single-pane plate glass shop window replaced the Georgian bay window glazed with small panes. All the technical conditions existed for the use of large areas of glass in the façades of buildings.

In the twentieth century numerous technical innovations by Ford, Libbey-Owens, Pilkington, and Pittsburgh Plate Glass have made a great expansion of the industry possible.

A four-storeyed plate-glass façade was used in the Tietz Department Store in Berlin in 1896; however, it was the plain glass curtain wall of Gropius' Bauhaus in Dessau in 1925 which set the future pattern [B4].

The clean, manufactured appearance appealed to the pioneers of modern architecture; the serious functional problems created by the glass curtain wall (*see* Sections 5.1 and 2) were appreciated only in the fifties, when the area of glass was once more reduced to more rational proportions.

In parallel with the glass-metal construction developed the use of glass in conjunction with reinforced concrete. Auguste Perret [B33] was one of the first to appreciate the potentialities of combining glass and concrete.

Fig. 6.5. 32 ft. diameter reinforced concrete dome, 2¼ in. thick with 4⅜ in. diameter glass lenses. Nettlewell Grammar School at Harrow, England, built by Lenscrete Ltd. in 1956.

The strength of glass was utilized by M. Joachim, who patented in 1908 *le béton translucide*, which combined glass lenses with reinforced concrete, and relied on the compressive strength of glass (Fig. 6.5).

6.4. Plastics and other Synthetics

Plastics may be defined as materials which can be formed plastically at a moderate temperature, much below that required for softening metals or glass, but turn hard at normal temperatures. Asphalt was known to the ancient Assyrians, and shellac, used in the early phonograph records, was used in many parts of the world.

Even synthetic thermoplastic materials have been known for a century. In 1865, Alexander Parkes produced Parkesine in England (from nitrocellulose, camphor and alcohol) in search of a synthetic substitute for horn, and in 1869 John Wyatt produced in America a similar material in search of a substance to make billiard balls without ivory, which he called celluloid. Acrylic plastics, the transparent materials known by the trade names of perspex or plexiglass, were developed by Otto Röhm in Germany in 1927.

The successful use of plastics in building is, however, so recent that it is not yet possible to evaluate their true significance. In the last twenty years plastics have been used to an increasing extent for builders' hardware, for transparent or translucent roof sheets, as flooring materials, for table and wall surfaces, and to a lesser extent for external facing where durability remains a serious problem. Perhaps the most important applications have been less obvious, in joint sealants, in adhesives, and as protective coatings.

Although fully plastic houses have been produced for exhibition purposes, the significance of synthetics in building lies more in their great variety. It is, at least theoretically, possible to tailor chemicals to fit the required properties. The success of aluminium curtain walls depends at least as much on the joint sealant and the insulation as it does on the glass or metal.

6.5. Timber—A Traditional Material in a New Form

Timber is the oldest of all the traditional building materials. Although a natural material, it can be produced by afforestation. It has a warm feeling and infinite variety of texture. Unfortunately it is subject to attack by insects and fungi, it burns readily, it suffers from mechanical defects which are not predictable, and it shrinks and warps with moisture changes, so that it seemed at one time to have no place in an increasingly industrialized building industry, except for small houses made by traditional methods.

The fact that no timber survived in ancient buildings seems less serious when we have better methods of fire-fighting and pest control, and when moreover the overwhelming majority of buildings are not intended to last for more than a century. The variability of the natural product and the dimensional changes suffered by it, however, are serious obstacles to standardised factory production.

The variable strength of timber has been overcome to some extent by the development of mechanical stress grading machines which classify the timber pieces by measuring their stiffness.

The more important development, however, is the use of high-strength synthetic adhesives to bond together timber into plywood or laminated structural members. The use of several layers averages out the effect of defects and the effect of grain, reduces dimensional changes, and increases the size of the timber member beyond the limits set by the size of the tree.

The difference between veneering an inferior timber with a high-quality surface, a technique already known to the ancient Egyptians, and laminated plywood, lies in the strength of the modern product. Chairs were made from laminated timber in the Russian Baltic about 1875; but the industrial production of plywood dates from about 1910. Otto Hetzer patented a process in Germany in 1905 for making structural members from timber laminations joined with casein glue. In the post-war years adhesives based on urea or phenol-resorcinol formaldehyde have been commonly used, and the industry owes a great deal to synthetics (Fig. 6.6).

Less spectacular has been the growth of a new industry since

Fig. 6.6.   Eagle Aviary, Bristol Zoo, England. (Architects: Saxon, Smith and Partners, Chester.) Note that curves, not necessarily conforming to any regular form, are easily produced in laminated timber.

the forties for making composition board out of wood chips, which also depended on the development of suitable bonding agents. These boards may be regarded as reconstituted timber in much the same way as concrete is reconstituted stone, and they have the same advantages of producing large jointless units with cheap and abundant raw materials.

6.6. The Industrialization of Building

Since the beginning of the nineteenth century the productivity of labour has greatly increased in nearly all industries through the use of mechanical power and mass production techniques. It is sometimes held that the building industry is handicapped by the unpredictability of the weather; but this has not prevented a great reduction in site labour in the building of roads or dams, where machines have largely taken over. Nor is the traditional nature of the industry purely to blame, because it has in fact changed to an extent where building craftsmen trained by eighteenth century methods would be of very little use on a modern building site.

If industrialization has not made the progress that was hoped for a hundred years ago, attempts to remove the production of buildings to the factory have not been lacking. The use of iron immediately transferred a large part of the work to the foundry and the machine shop, starting with Darby's cast iron bridge at Coalbrookdale (*see* Section 2.1); the time required to erect a modern steel frame is small compared with the time taken up by the fabrication of the steel.

In the middle of the nineteenth century the building of timber houses also changed through the development of the balloon frame in America. Timber was now cut in the saw mill by high speed machinery, and assembled by machine-made nails instead of the traditional laborious mortised and tenoned joints.

Reinforced concrete, which came into use only in the latter part of the nineteenth century, was produced in prefabricated units from the early years of the twentieth. J. L. Peterson [6.2] on the occasion of the fiftieth anniversary of the American Concrete Institute, described precast buildings in America dating from 1907, and a complete system for a factory-produced home patented in 1912 (Fig. 6.7).

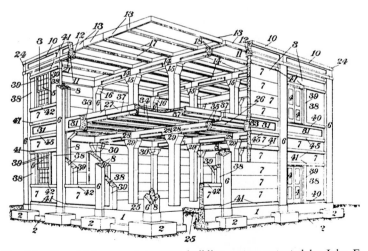

Fig. 6.7. Completely precast concrete building system patented by John E. Conzelman in 1912. (From the Anniversary Issue of the *Journal of the American Concrete Institute* [6.2].)

The Great London Exhibition of 1851 showed remarkable progress in industrialized building. The Crystal Palace, which housed it, was completely prefabricated to a modular design, based on three standardized truss lengths (Fig. 6.8); even mechanical

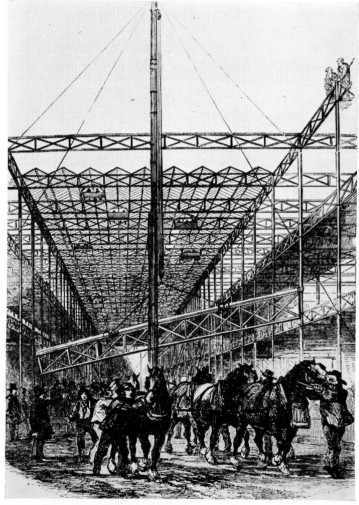

Fig. 6.8. Erection of the structure of the Crystal Palace, late 1850. (From a contemporary woodcut, reproduced by Hobhouse [6.10].)

erection procedures were used. Among the exhibits was a completely prefabricated iron church for use by missionary organizations in the colonies.

Prefabricated houses for shipping to distant lands from the mother country where not unusual in the nineteenth century. The Old Government House, still preserved in Melbourne, which was the residence of the first Governor of Victoria, Charles Joseph La Trobe, was shipped from England in sections and erected in 1840. It was, like all prefabricated buildings of the time, a modestly sized house.

6.7. System Building

The limitations of factory produced housing are least apparent with timber, which is the predominant house-building material in America and Scandinavia. It is relatively light, joints can be nailed, and dimensional errors corrected by site-cutting.

While steel and concrete houses need more precision in manufacture, and more mechanical aids for erection, prefabricated houses, particularly in concrete, have been made for more than fifty years in small quantities. In 1919 the shortage caused by the suspension of house building during the war and the promise of adequate housing for returned soldiers, encouraged greater attention to non-traditional methods of building.

In 1942 the British Government appointed a committee "to consider materials and methods of construction suitable for the building of houses and flats, having regard to efficiency, economy and speed of erection, and to make recommendations for post-war practice". The committee reported a surprising variety of non-traditional houses built in the inter-war years; but none had been produced in batches of more than a few hundred, and the total quantity was small [6.3].

In the post-war period an extensive programme of prefabrication was launched in England with government support, partly to provide houses more quickly and partly to make use of the facilities available in aircraft and other factories no longer required after the cessation of hostilities. Most of the houses, particularly those made of metal, met with a poor public reception, and the cost did not compare favourably with traditional construction. "Prefab" became a dirty word, and it took many years before industrialized housing could again be seriously considered.

In the United States also, factory-produced housing did not prove either popular or profitable. However, in Russia and in Eastern Europe the factory-production of concrete dwelling units was generally adopted [6.4, 6.5].

In 1962 Professor Ovsyankin forecast [6.6] that by 1965 half the buildings in the U.S.S.R. would be erected with factory-produced large panels. The reason for the Russian success lies largely in the degree of control which the government can exercise over the production, construction and letting of the housing units, which ensures large-scale production (Fig. 6.9). Careful thought is given to erection with large cranes, and the machines can be put to intensive use on large housing estates.

In the last few years industrialized building has come back into favour in Western Europe [6.7, 6.8], particularly in France. Large concrete panels for residential construction appear to be more successful in high-rise buildings where a substantial site organization is in any case required, and adaptation of units to individual requirements is not expected.

The problem is more difficult for the small house. Due to increasing production of components in the factory, the cost of direct labour in traditional construction in England now comprises only about one quarter of the total. With fully industrialized houses, material costs are often higher. For example, more reinforced concrete may be needed in factory-produced housing because of the lack of continuity and the handling stresses, and non-traditional materials, such as light metal and plastics, have so far proved quite expensive by comparison. If a manufacturer of factory-produced buildings was able to produce and market a product with the same functional characteristics and the same quality as traditional building, but at a considerably lower cost, he should be able to win an increasing share of the market, and even cater for part of

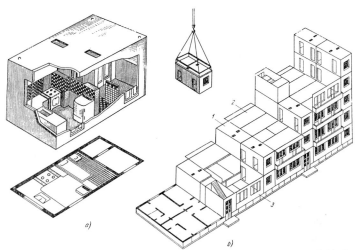

Fig. 6.9. Erection of flats from cells, including fully prefabricated kitchen-bathroom units, in Russia. (From *Neue Methoden der Montage von Gebäuden in der UdSSR* [6.4].)

the potential demand which does not become effective because of the present cost. For most consumer goods the custom-made article is two or three times as expensive as the mass-produced one; but in housing there is at present virtually no difference. In the circumstance the client shows little inclination to sacrifice his personal choice of detail without corresponding advantage in terms of cost.

In house-building the small builder, whose organization is simple and whose contact with the client is direct, has considerable advantages. A study made by the Harvard Graduate School of Business Administration is illuminating [6.9]: –

"The production manager (of Sunshine Builders Inc., a Florida building contractor) explained that by and large 'prefabbing' does not pay unless the customer is not permitted to make any changes in the house he buys. If Sunshine adopted such a policy we would lose sales. Also the size of our line argues against our relying on prefabbing. For instance, prefabbed roof trusses, which many construction firms use, are more expensive than 'on-site' construction because we have so many models."

6.8. Modular Coordination

A much greater measure of standardization has been suggested as an intermediate step between a prefabricated system, in which everything is predetermined, and fabrication on the site by traditional methods. The question of an international, or at least a regional or national, standard for modular sizes must be settled before this can be implemented.

The initial impetus came from Albert Farwell Bemis, an American industrialist, who started to take interest in the dimensional coordination of building materials and equipment about 1921. In 1936 he published the final part, "Rational Design", of a three-volume study entitled "The Evolving House". In this he proposed the Cubical Modular Method "to improve the inefficient methods of assembly of unrelated materials and reduce the cost of building construction by applying industrial production techniques". He considered that four inches provided the largest dimensional increment for minimizing problems resulting from stocking and distributing standardized components, while preserving design flexibility to meet practical and aesthetic requirements. At the time he also considered a three-inch module which subsequently found much favour in British Commonwealth countries, where many dimensions are geared to the English standard nine-inch by three-inch brick. However, the four-inch module was generally adopted as a standard in the late forties and early fifties because it differs by only 1.6% from 10 cm which constitutes the obvious metric module.

After Bemis' death in 1936, his family established the Modular Service Association, which cooperated with the American Standards Association in calling a conference in 1939 to set up a study project with support from the American Institute of Architects and the Producers' Council Inc. [B56].

The concept of modular standardization struck a responsive chord in the European countries faced with a vast rebuilding programme, and the European Productivity Agency of the Organization for European Economic Cooperation set up Project 174 in 1953. This resulted in the fairly general acceptance of 4 in. and 10 cm as alternative modules, and encouraged further national studies [B57]. In traditional construction lack of fit is overcome by cutting to size materials, such as timber, on the site, adjusting the width of joints, as in brickwork, or providing a cover piece, as in skirting boards. Only the last method is available in prefabricated dry construction. When a complete system building is produced, the manufacturer has full control over the design, production and, often, the erection. In attempting to assemble a building from modular components made by different manufacturers, there must be a clear understanding of the tolerances of the production process, the distortion during transport and erection, and the relative movement of different parts due to temperature and moisture. The components themselves must be smaller than an exact multiple of the four-inch module by a clearly defined amount to allow them to fit into a modular space.

6.9. Systems of Proportion and Preferred Dimensions

No standardization can be achieved if every multiple of four inches is an admissible modular size, and one effect of modular coordination has been a renewed interest in the classical systems of proportioning and preferred sizes. The relation between the human scale (Fig. 6.10) and the proportions of buildings is already considered by Vitruvius, in Book III, Chapter 1, *On Symmetry; In Temples and in the Human Body* [B5]: –

"Therefore, since nature has designed the human body so that its members are duly proportioned to the frame as a whole, it appears that the Ancients had good reason for their rule, that in perfect buildings the different members must be in exact symmetrical relations to the whole general scheme. Hence, while transmitting to us the proper arrangements for buildings of all kinds, they were particularly careful to do so in the case of temples of the gods, buildings in which merits and faults usually last forever." (p. 73.)

Vitruvius then proceeds to set out the proportions of the orders, and the arrangement of the columns in plan.

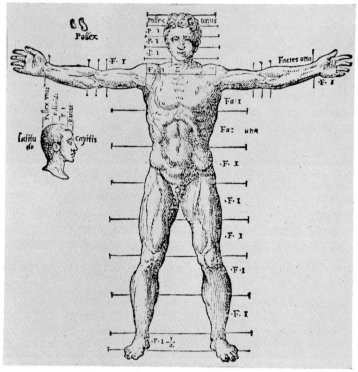

Fig. 6.10. Proportions of the human figure. (From Barbaro's edition of Vitruvius' *De Architectura*, Venice 1567.)

The concept that certain ratios produce harmony both in music and in architecture is mentioned by Alberti [B6]: –

"The Rule of these Proportions is best gathered from those Things in which we find Nature herself to be most compleat and admirable; and indeed I am every Day more convinced of the Truth of Pythagoras' Saying that Nature is sure to act consistently, and with a constant Analogy in all her Operations: From whence I conclude that, the same Numbers, by means of which the Agreement of Sounds affects our Ears with Delight, are the very same which please our Eyes and Our Mind. We shall therefore borrow all our Rules for finishing our Proportions, from the Musicians,

who are the greatest Masters of this Sort of Numbers, ..."
(pp. 196–7.)

Professor Wittkower [6.11] inclines to the view that the proportions in Palladio's work, which greatly influenced subsequent design, are based on the harmonic proportion $5 : 3 = 1.666 \ldots$, rather than on the Golden Rule of 1.618.

Some incommensurable proportions date from the Renaissance. We have evidence of the architectural use of the ratio $\theta = 1 + \sqrt{2}$, derived from the diagonal of the square, by Leonardo da Vinci (*see* Fig. 1.10).

The construction which yields the ratio $\varphi = \frac{1}{2}(1 + \sqrt{5}) = 1.618 \ldots$ is found in Book IV of Euclid's *Elements* (about 300 B.C.) for drawing the regular polygon. The relationship is mentioned several times in the sixteenth century; but interest in it seems to have been directed primarily towards attempts to square the circle [6.12].

There is no real evidence of its use in architectural design until the mid-nineteenth century. The precise origin of the classical systems of proportion and their relation to the human scale is complicated by the tendency of Renaissance authors to ascribe their ideas to the Ancients because of the authority enjoyed by Greek and Roman precedent, and by the subsequent tendency of the nineteenth century to adduce archaeological precedent. Constructions have been published during the last hundred years to prove that Greek and Renaissance architecture was designed by the Golden Section; but there is also a substantial literature to prove that other proportions were used [B58]. We can only say with certainty that it was used for much of the Revival Architecture after 1850, and the prestige it enjoys seems to owe more to the fascination with the mysteries of mathematics than to the realities of classical design.

The Golden Section was suggested as the basis for modular coordination by Le Corbusier in 1950 [6.13]. Even when the incommensurable quantities are replaced by real numbers, however, it does not seem an adequate basis for the proportions of industrialized building.

Le Corbusier's use of the Fibonacci series, which has become largely associated with the Golden Section in the literature on classical theories of proportion, is on much stronger ground. The concept has been elaborated by Ezra Ehrenkrantz [6.14] into a modular number pattern, whereby the admissible modular dimensions become more widely spaced with increasing size. This overcomes the difficulty of Bemis' original proposal to make every multiple of 4 in. an admissible modular size, whereby the nearest modular size above 8 in. is 12 in. (an increase of 50%), but the nearest modular size above 240 in. is 244 in. (an increase of less than 2%).

It seems likely that a successful solution will have to abandon the classical theory, and approach the problem experimentally. Certain dimensions can be fixed permanently because they depend on the human figure. These include floor-to-ceiling heights for all normal storeys and the dimensions of all but ceremonial staircases. For others, e.g. window sizes, we must admit a small number of preferred sizes in 4 in. increments. For small dimensions, e.g. wall-thickness, we have to accept increments of 1 in., but still with a strictly defined range of preferred sizes. On close examination the number of preferred sizes essential for full design potential is found to be much smaller than is commonly believed. The economy which results from exact structural sizes is often overestimated. The cost of the extra concrete due to adopting the nearest higher 4 in. increment is compensated by the use of standard formwork. Steel must be encased for fire-protection in multi-storey buildings, and it is the casing which must be modular. We then determine combinations of two, three, four or five modular component sizes which add up to the preferred dimensions. We can thus develop number patterns to find, for example, methods of cladding walls with modular components which allow doors, windows and partitions to be inserted without cutting factory-produced units or making specials [6.15]. With a computer such number patterns can be readily tabulated.

While the mathematical theories of classical architecture no longer appear relevant, some of the principles still apply. Its main visual elements were the Five Orders whose proportions had been refined by long use. The principal visual elements on the façade of most modern high-rise buildings are windows and sunshading devices; yet many of these units, and particularly shading devices, have not received the necessary care in design to fit them for this aesthetic function.

Structural mechanics imposes on the high-rise building an inescapable discipline. Professor Curt Siegel [6.16] recently examined to what extent the expression of the structure takes the place of the classical rules of proportion.

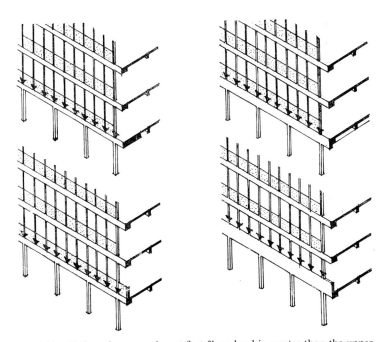

Fig. 6.11. If the column spacing at first-floor level is greater than the upper-floor grid, a bigger spandrel is needed. This can be hidden by using greater width, or else an upstand beam behind the curtain wall *(left)*. However, this conveys a feeling of weakness, and it is better to express the bigger structural member on the elevation *(right)*. (Reproduced from H. J. Cowan, *Presidential Address to Section* Engineering and Architecture, *Australian Journal of Science*, Vol. 26 (1964), p. 209.)

Structural rules are not governed by direct proportions. For example, if we take a bookshelf and enlarge every dimension fifty times, i.e. increase the depth and the span of the planks fifty times, the deflection due to their own weight is increased fifty times, and the stress in the timber is also increased fifty times. This is no longer a practical structure, and it must be redesigned to give more supports or much deeper beams.

The main rhythm of the multi-storey façade is provided by column grids and spandrel depths, and structural theory determines their dimensions. The true size can be concealed, but this has a disturbing effect. For example, the span of the first floor beams is often increased for the sake of greater freedom of planning at ground-floor level. Since the span is longer than in the upper floors, the size of the spandrels must be increased. The structural engineer can make the spandrels the same depth at a small extra cost (Fig. 6.11). However, the constant spandrel depth conveys a feeling of weakness once the structural problem is appreciated, and this is removed only by a correct expression of structural depth.

6.10. A Comprehensive Design Concept for Architecture

The dichotomy of thought which developed in the late eighteenth century between architects and the designers of industrial structures (*see* Section 2.2) is only now beginning to be resolved. In the middle of the nineteenth century the production of buildings was as far advanced towards industrialization as that of most other commodities. The introduction of factory-produced ready-made clothing was roughly contemporary with the Crystal Palace; but while one was in the mainstream of development, the latter was remote from the architectural spirit of its age. It was not designed by an architect, and for another half-century architects could see no merit in the new technology, although they gradually used it for structural support hidden behind a façade.

The resistance of the architectural orthodoxy to the inevitable changes was unfortunate, because it led to a revolution of architectural thinking instead of a gradual absorption of scientific ideas.

The impact of industrialization on architectural practice was uppermost in the minds of the pioneers of modern architecture in the early years of this century [6.17]. The new age was conceived as being dominated by the machine, and the new architect as a creative artist who understood machine-made materials and the potentialities of mass-production. It was not a basic part of this concept that the architect should be equally at home designing stainless-steel spoons and stainless-steel curtain walls; but this aspect has often been strongly emphasised.

The ideas of the nineteen-twenties no longer suffice in the sixties. Buildings conceived merely in terms of structure and finishes, combining surfaces to divide and envelop space, do not satisfy even in their material aspects the requirements of our time. Technology has reached the stage where buildings no longer fall down; but they are often exceedingly uncomfortable and inconvenient, because well-known laws of nineteenth-century physics have been ignored in the mid-twentieth century.

Since industrialization is dependent on mass production, we must consider whether the design of great architectural masterpieces as timeless works of art can be separated any longer from the design of the utilitarian buildings which form the bulk of the building industry's output. The conflict between the traditional philosophy of architecture and engineering has been fairly stated by Gio Ponti [6.18]: –

"Engineering is eclectic; architecture is not. Engineering accepts, experiments with and incorporates, naturally and legitimately, the best available solutions offered by technology and industry, whereby it discharges its whole duty. Engineering creates technical works which are repeatable, multipliable and surpassable. Its works continuously outdo their predecessors. Architecture, being art, is not progressive and tends to create only perpetual unities, expressions which stand by themselves, irrepeatable. It creates works of art that cannot be surpassed, because its expression is an end in itself, and therefore perpetual. It is ridiculous to think of progress in music, painting and poetry. . . . There is a history of painting, music and poetry, but there is no progress in painting, music and poetry."

The client who wishes to build a factory or an office building is entitled to ask for progress. He must have a building conceived in accordance with the latest engineering concepts to be competitive. He will almost certainly demolish it when it no longer fulfils its purpose. If he has to choose between commodity and delight, he must chose commodity.

Industrialized architecture cannot succeed unless it produces commodity, firmness *and* delight, all at a reasonable cost, and this requires consideration of a much wider range of scientific problems than we have thought necessary in the past.

We can study the gradual evolution of architectural science over a period of several centuries. While we may turn out to be no wiser than past generations, we can at least learn from their mistakes.

Glossary

This glossary of technical terms is intended to assist the general reader.

Bending Moment: Moment caused by the loads acting on the structure.

Buckling: Failure of compression member by deflection at right angles to the direction of the load.

Built-in: Rigidly restrained at the ends to prevent rotation.

Cantilever: Portion of beam overhanging support.

Cast Iron: Containing more carbon than steel, and consequently less ductile and weaker in tension; used as a structural material in the 18th and 19th centuries.

Catenary: Curve assumed by a cable hanging under its own weight.

Coefficient of Variation: Statistical measure of the degree of dispersion of experimental data.

Cross section: Section at right angles to the span.

Curtain Wall: Thin external wall hung from a skeleton frame; the frame supports the roof and the floors above (see Loadbearing Wall).

Daylight Factor: Ratio of illumination on a horizontal plane inside to the simultaneous exterior illumination.

Dead Weight: The weight of the structure, as distinct from the useful load carried by it.

Decibel: Unit for measuring sound levels; sound level meters are normally calibrated in decibels.

Dial Gauge: A mechanical device for deflection measurement employing a train of gears.

Elastic deformation: Deformation fully recovered when the load is removed.

Electric resistance strain gauge: Very light electrical device for strain measurement which can be glued to the structure; it is based on the change in electrical resistance due to the variation in cross-sectional area resulting from the strain of the wire.

Entasis: A slight swelling of the shaft of a column, used by Greek and Renaissance architects to avoid a hollow appearance.

Extensometer: Device for measuring strain.

Factor of Safety: Ratio of stress at failure to maximum permissible stress.

Fixing Moment: Redundant moment at the end of a member, due to the restraint of the support or of an adjoining member.

Flexure: Bending.

Formwork: Temporary structure used during construction, in particular for supporting wet concrete.

Hinge: Joint allowing free rotation.

Hooke's Law: Stress is proportional to strain (*see* Section 1.5).

Hoop force: The internal horizontal force in a dome.

Hyperbolic paraboloid: Doubly curved surface formed entirely by straight lines (*see* Section 4.8).

Jack arch: Short-span arch supporting floor between closely spaced beams.

Keystone: Stone at the top of a masonry arch.

Lantern: Small open or glazed structure crowning a roof, particularly a dome.

Lever arm: Distance between the resultant tensile and compressive flexural forces in a cross-section.

Lintel: A short-span beam, usually over a door or window opening.

Load-Bearing Wall: Wall strong enough to support the roof and the floors above it.

Longitudinal: Parallel to the span.

Lumen: Unit of light, e.g. a measure of the light output of a lamp; illumination is normally measured with photometers in lumens per square foot.

Maximum permissible stress: The greatest stress admitted by building regulations.

Membrane structure: Structure free from bending.

Meridianal force: Internal force along the meridian of a dome, at right angles to the hoop force.

Mild steel: Low carbon steel of moderate strength and high ductility.

Modulus of elasticity: Measure of elastic deformation, defined as the stress which would produce a unit strain.

Moment: Force multiplied by distance at which it acts.

Moment distribution: Popular method for designing statically indeterminate structures (*see* Section 3.9).

Moment of resistance: Internal moment in a beam, which for equilibrium must equal the bending moment applied to the beam.

Monolithic: Cast in one piece, and therefore continuous.

Neutral Axis: Line at which flexure stress changes from tension to compression.

Normal reinforced concrete: Concrete reinforced with steel which is not pre-stressed.

Pin-joint: A joint allowing free rotation, whether formed by a pin or not.

Plain concrete: Concrete without reinforcement.

Plastic deformation: Deformation not recovered when the load is removed.

Precast concrete: Concrete placed in position after casting, instead of being cast in place.

Prestressed Concrete: Concrete reinforced with prestressed steel (*see* Section 3.4).

Reaction: Force exerted by the ground or a supporting member in opposition to the loads.

Redundant structure: A structure which by virtue of an excess of members, rigid joints or reactions, is statically indeterminate. The excessive members, rigid joints or reactions are *redundancies.*

Rigid frame: A frame in which some or all of the joints are rigid; it is in consequence statically indeterminate.

Rigid joint: A joint allowing no rotation of the members joined relative to one another, i.e. a right-angle joint remains a right-angle joint under load.

Rise: The height of an arch or dome above the springings.

Shell: Thin curved structural surface.

Simply supported: Supported in a manner which permits free rotation.

Springings: Supports of an arch or dome.

Sprinkler Head: Outlet attached to a water pipe which produces a spray for extinguishing a fire; can be operated from a valve, or opened automatically by a device which fuses or breaks at a predetermined temperature.

Statically determinate: Soluble by statics alone, i.e. by resolving horizontally and vertically, and taking moments about one convenient point.

Statically indeterminate: Insoluble by statics alone, because there are more unknown members, rigid joints or reactions, than statical equations.

Strain: Deformation per unit length.

Stress: Force per unit area.

Stress Reversal: Change from compressive to tensile stress, or vice versa.

Theorem of Three Moments: Popular method for determining moments in continuous beams (*see* Section 3.7).

Thrust: Compressive force.

Transverse: Perpendicular to the span.

Truss: Structure formed by an assembly of tension and compression members to resist bending.

Ultimate strength: The maximum strength of the structure, which occurs immediately prior to failure.

Voussoir: Wedge-shaped block of masonry forming part of an arch or dome.

Working stress: Stress due to the loads normally acting on the structure; normally synonymous with the maximum permissible stress.

Wrought iron: Containing less carbon than steel, and consequently weaker; used as a structural material in the 18th and 19th centuries; is more ductile than cast iron and has better tensile strength.

Yield stress: Stress at which substantial plastic deformation first occurs; is commonly used as the upper limit of the elastic behaviour of the material, and as the criterion for its failure.

Zenith: Point in the sky directly above the observer, i.e. at altitude 90°.

Bibliography

General Bibliography on the History of Building Science

Since architectural science is concerned with numerous aspects of science and of construction, the literature from which its history may be gathered is enormous. I assumed that the reader would be willing to accept the dates of the first water closet and of the Euler formula without documentation; but I have given references to important sources, particularly where they are obscure. European and American readers should have no undue difficulty in locating them; Australians are in a less fortunate position. I am grateful to the British Museum, the John Rylands Library in Manchester, and the Department of Rare Books, Cornell University, for permission to use their facilities. The following pages are intended to guide the reader who may wish to collect further information on the history of building science.

General

Many of the facts can be gathered from a good encyclopaedia. Since many of the crucial developments occurred in the 19th century, an old encyclopaedia describes some historical facts as recent technological advances. The Ninth Edition of the Britannica is particularly helpful, and still available in many libraries. It also gives more space to details of classical and medieval history than a modern edition.

B1. *Encyclopaedia Britannica*. 25 volumes. Ninth Edition. Adam and Charles Black, Edinburgh, 1875–88.

Architecture

Banister Fletcher remains one of the best sources for factual information on traditional architecture, but the reader has ample choice. There are fewer good reference books on modern architecture.

B2. BANISTER FLETCHER: *A History of Architecture by the Comparative Method.* 17th Edition. Athlone Press, London 1961. 1366 pp.

B3. G. HATJE (Editor): *Encyclopaedia of Modern Architecture.* Thames and Hudson, London. 336 pp.

B4. J. JOEDICKE: *A History of Modern Architecture.* Architectural Press, London 1959. 243 pp.

For an understanding of the history of architectural science before the 19th century, direct reference to Vitruvius and Alberti is helpful. Both are now readily obtainable.

B5. MARCUS VITRUVIUS POLLIO (Transl. by M. H. Morgan): *The Ten Books of Architecture*. Dover Publications, New York 1960. 331 pp. *This is a modern translation, based on the original first-century text, as far as that can be ascertained, and deleting Renaissance additions.*

B6. LEONE BATTISTA ALBERTI (Transl. by J. Leoni): *Ten Books on Architecture*. Alec Tiranti, London, 1955. 256 pp. *This is a facsimile of the first English edition of 1755.* Alberti reputedly presented the *Ten Books* to Pope Nicholas V in 1452. It was first printed in Florence in Latin in 1485, and in Italian in Venice in 1546. Leoni, a Venetian architect, used the Italian version.

Science and Technology

There is now a vast literature on the history of science and technology , including several specialized journals. I have mainly used:

B7. R. J. FORBES AND E. J. DIJKSTERHUIS: *A History of Science and Technology*. Penguin Books, London 1963. 2 volumes. 536 pp.

B8. H. T. PLEDGE: *Science since 1500*. H.M. Stationery Office, London 1939. 357 pp.

Mathematics and Elasticity

Rouse Ball on mathematics, and Todhunter and Pearson on elasticity are excellent source books, but both exclude the 20th century—perhaps not a very serious omission in our field. One of the science or engineering texts (B7, B8, B14, B15 and B16) will suffice for briefer reference.

B9. W. W. ROUSE BALL: *A Short Account of the History of Mathematics*. Dover Publications, New York 1960. 522 pp. *A reprint of the 4th edition of 1908.*

B10. I. TODHUNTER AND K. PEARSON: *A History of the Theory of Elasticity*. Dover Publications, New York 1960. 3 volumes, 2244 pp. *A reprint of the 1886–93 edition.*

Engineering

In addition to the specialized studies listed below, there are three recent popular books with wider coverage. Camp's "Ancient Engineers" include those of the Renaissance. Pannell is primarily concerned with public works, and with Britain. Armytage deals mainly with heavy industry.

B11. L. SPRAGUE DE CAMP: *The Ancient Engineers*. Rigby, Adelaide 1963. 408 pp. *Original edition published in America by Doubleday, 1960.*

B12. J. P. M. PANNELL: *An Illustrated History of Civil Engineering*. Thames and Hudson, London 1964. 376 pp.

B13. W. H. G. ARMYTAGE: *A Social History of Engineering*. Faber and Faber, London 1961. 378 pp.

The Transactions of the Newcomen Society are a fruitful source of detailed information on British history. In addition to *Smiles' Lives of the Engineers*, there are now several well-documented and less wordy modern studies.

Structures

There are still only a few books on the history of structures. Giedion has a pronounced bias towards architecture, Timoshenko and the Russian-language Bernshtein towards mathematics. For our purpose, Straub's is the most balanced presentation. Many modern textbooks, particularly those by American authors, have a short historical note.

B14. S. TIMOSHENKO: *History of the Strength of Materials*. McGraw-Hill, New York 1953. 452 pp.

B15. S. A. BERNSHTEIN: *Ocherki po istorii stroitelnoi mekhaniki*. Gosudarstvence izdatelstvo literatury po stroitelstvu i arkhitektury, Moscow 1957. 236 pp.

B16. H. STRAUB: *A History of Civil Engineering*. Leonard Hill, London 1952. 258 pp.

B17. S. GIEDION: *Space, Time and Architecture*. Harvard University Press, Cambridge 1962. 4th edition. 778 pp.

Two source-books are noteworthy: the original Castigliano, still obtainable in most libraries which have been in existence for 40 years, and the recently published selection of Cross' original papers.

B18. A. CASTIGLIANO: *Elastic Stresses in Structures*. Scott, Greenwood and Son, London 1919. 360 pp. *Translation by E. S. Andrews of the French version published in Turin in 1879.*

B19. Selected papers by HARDY CROSS: *Arches, Continuous Frames, Columns and Conduits*. University of Illinois Press, Urbana 1963. 265 pp.

Building Materials

All the published books on the history of building materials concentrate either on medieval craft practice or on archeology. The best is by Davey, a Fellow of the Society of Antiquaries, who was for many years Principal Scientific Officer at the British Building Research Station.

B20. N. DAVEY: *A History of Building Materials*. Phoenix House, London 1961. 260 pp.

Iron, Steel and Concrete

Schubert covers the early history of iron and steel making. Tredgold, a standard work on cast iron in its day, is in many old-established libraries. The history of the steel frame in Chicago is well documented. The development of semi-rigid design and of the plastic theory is described by Baker.

B21. H. R. SCHUBERT: *History of the British Iron and Steel Industry from c. 450 B.C. to A.D. 1775*. Routledge and Kegan Paul, London 1957. 445 pp.

B22. T. TREDGOLD: *Practical Essay on the Strength of Cast Iron*. J. Taylor, London 1824. 305 pp.

B23. F. A. RANDALL: *History of the Development of Building Construction in Chicago*. University of Illinois Press, Chicago 1949. 385 pp.

B24. C. W. CONDIT: *The Chicago School of Architecture*. University of Chicago Press, 1964. 238 pp.

B25. J. F. BAKER: *The Steel Skeleton*. Cambridge University Press, London 1954 and 1956. 2 vol. 206 pp. + 408 pp.

Early text-books on reinforced concrete are still quite common, Berger and Guillerme was the first major book, and Marsh the first major English book. Hamilton gives a brief history of the early work. The ICE report is indispensable for understanding the slow acceptance of reinforced concrete in England.

The French centenary number includes an excellent survey of the architectural use of concrete. Raafat's treatment is less authoritative, but more accessible. Collins deals mainly with the work of Perret.

B26. C. BERGER AND V. GUILLERME: *La Construction en Ciment Armé*. Ch. Dunod Paris 1902. 2 vol., 886 pp. + 69 plates.

B27. C. F. MARSH: *Reinforced Concrete*. Constable, London 1904. 545 pp.

B28. S. B. HAMILTON: *A Note on the History of Reinforced Concrete in Buildings*. H.M. Stationery Office, London 1956. 40 pp.

B29. S. B. HAMILTON: *A Short History of the Structural Fire Protection of Building*. H.M. Stationery Office, London 1958. 73 pp.

B30. Institution of Civil Engineers: *Preliminary and Second Reports of the Committee on Reinforced Concrete*. The Institution, London 1913. 262 + 187 pp.

B31. Chambre Syndicale des Constructeurs en Ciment Armé de France: *Cent Ans de Béton Armé*. Editions Science et Industrie, Paris 1949. 214 pp.

B32. A. A. RAAFAT: *Reinforced Concrete in Architecture*. Reinhold, New York 1958. 240 pp.

B33. P. COLLINS: *Concrete, the Vision of a New Architecture*. Faber and Faber, London 1959. 307 pp.

A book by Möll, President of the German patent court, describes prestressed concrete patents registered in Germany. An early English view of the problems of prestressed concrete is given in the record of the ICE conference; it includes an historical sketch.

B34. H. MÖLL: *Spannbeton*. Berliner Union, Stuttgart 1954. 272 pp.

B35. Joint Committee on Materials etc.: *Conference on Prestressed Concrete*. Institution of Civil Engineers, London 1949. 132 pp.

Johansen's yield-line theory for the ultimate strength of reinforced concrete slabs, originally published in Denmark in 1943 and virtually unobtainable, has been republished, this time in English.

B36. K. W. JOHANSEN: *Yield-line Theory*. Cement and Concrete Association, London 1962. 181 pp.

Shell Roofs and Suspension Structures

The book published by Dywidag on their 90th anniversary gives details of the first shell roofs. A post-war view of the problem is given in the report of two conferences held in 1954 in America and in England. The former contains an early account of Candela's shells.

The original ideas for suspension structures are described by Otto.

Recent developments in both fields are recorded in the *Bulletins of the International Association of Shell Structures*, published in Madrid since 1960.

B37. G. VON KLASS: *Weit spannt sich der Bogen*. Dyckerhoff und Widmann, Munich 1955. 234 pp.

B38. *Proceedings of the Conference on Thin Concrete Shells*. Massachusetts Institute of Technology. Cambridge 1954. 134 pp.

B39. P. J. WITT (Editor): *Proceedings of a Symposium on Concrete Shell Construction*. Cement and Concrete Association, London 1954. 258 pp.

B40. FREI OTTO: *Das hängende Dach*. Ullstein, Berlin 1954. 160 pp.

Analysis with Models and Computers

The pre-war Anglo-American approach is described by Pippard in a small book which is out of print, but obtainable in most libraries. Southern European ideas of the forties are described in papers presented at the Congresses of the International Association for Bridge and Structural Engineering at Liège (1948) and Cambridge (1952); these proceedings are readily available. A more detailed account is given in the less accessible proceedings of a congress held in 1955 in Venice.

B41. A. J. S. PIPPARD: *The Experimental Study of Structures*. Edward Arnold, London 1947. 114 pp.

B42. *I Modelli nella Tecnica*. Accademia Nazionale dei Lincei, Rome 1956. 2 Vol., 698 + 623 pp.

The literature on the use of computers for structural design is growing rapidly. I have used:

B43. D. M. BROTTON: *The Application of Digital Computers to Structural Engineering Problems*. E. and F. N. Spon, London 1962. 182 pp.

Other Building Materials

McGrath treats the long history of glass both from the technical and the architectural point of view. Most of the other materials discussed in Chapter 6 are too new to have a substantial history, and a good account of their development can be found in brochures obtainable from the relevant manufacturers, or from such bodies as the Timber Development Associations in England and in Australia.

B44. R. McGRATH and others: *Glass in Architecture and Decoration*. Architectural Press, London 1961. 712 pp.

Functional Efficiency of Buildings

In addition to the substantial literature on climatology, there are two books which trace the relation of architecture to climate:

B45. J. E. ARONIN: *Climate and Architecture*. Reinhold, New York 1953. 304 pp.

B46. V. OLGYAY: *Design with Climate*. Princeton University Press, 1963. 190 pp.

The Olgyay Brothers have published the fullest account of the history of sunshading devices:

B47. A. AND V. OLGYAY: *Solar Control and Shading Devices*. Princeton University Press, 1957. 201 pp.

Walsh, of the British National Physical Laboratory, has covered the development of daylight design. Parry Moon's standard work on illuminating engineering, first published in 1936, has recently been reprinted. The history of artificial lighting is covered in several places. O'Dea, of the Science Museum, London, has produced a pamphlet which is adequate for our purpose.

B48. J. W. T. WALSH: *The Science of Daylight*. Macdonald, London 1961. 285 pp.

B49. P. MOON: *The Scientific Basis of Illuminating Engineering*. Dover Publications, New York 1961. 608 pp.

B50. W. T. O'DEA: *A Short History of Lighting*. H.M. Stationery Office, London 1958. 40 pp.

Acoustics is considered in detail by Vitruvius [B 5], and his statements on this subject are much clearer than most of his text. I do not know of a good history of the ancient subject of acoustics. Richardson briefly mentions some medieval work, and Beranek discusses some acoustical mythology which has accumulated over the ages.

B51. E. G. RICHARDSON: Acoustics in modern life. *Science Progress*, Vol. 42 (1954), pp. 232–9.

B52. L. L. BERANEK: *Music, Acoustics and Architecture*. John Wiley, New York 1962. 586 pp.

Noise control is too recent a problem to have a substantial history. However, a good statement of the development of the problem is given in a recent British Command Paper:

B53. Committee on the Problem of Noise: *Noise—Final Report*. H.M. Stationery Office, London 1963. 235 pp.

Building Services

The older history of sanitation and water supply is described in B11 and B12, and the recent history is covered by Nielsen.

The history of heating and ventilation has been reviewed by Billington.

The firms founded by Otis and Carrier still exist, and pamphlets describing the early history of lifts and air-conditioning respectively can be obtained from them.

B54. L. S. NIELSEN: *Standard Plumbing Engineering Design*. McGraw-Hill, New York 1963. pp. 1–30.

B55. N. S. BILLINGTON: A historical review of the art of heating and ventilating. *Architectural Science Review*, Vol. 2 (1959), pp. 118–130.

Modular Co-ordination and Theories of Proportion

American progress in modular standardisation was reviewed in 1962 by the Modular Standards Association. European work is set out in the EPA Reports on Project 174.

B56. Modular Building Standards Association: *Modular Practice*. John Wiley, New York 1962. 198 pp.

B57. *Modular Coordination in Building—Second Report of EPA Project 174.* European Productivity Agency, Paris 1961. 224 pp. *Note that the First Report on Project 174 was published by the EPA in Paris in 1956.*

Schofield has made a critical review of the classical theories of proportion.

B58. P. H. SCHOFIELD: *The Theory of Proportion in Architecture.* Cambridge University Press, London 1958. 156 pp.

References

Chapter 1

1.1. R. J. MAINSTONE: Structural theory and design. *Architecture and Building*, Vol. 34 (1959), pp. 106–113, 186–195 and 214–221.

1.2. JOHN RUSKIN: *The Stones of Venice*. Abridged from the 1853 edition by J. G. Links. Collins, London 1960, p. 70.

1.3. H. J. COWAN: Ancient Roman "concrete". *Jnl. Royal Institute of British Architects*, Vol. 61 (1954), p. 120.

1.4. E. MACCURDY: *The Notebooks of Leonardo da Vinci*. Reprint Society, London 1954. 2 vol., 610 + 566 pp.

1.5. CHARLES AUGUSTIN DE COULOMB: Sur une application des règles de maximis et minimis à quelques problèmes de statique à l'architecture. *Mémoires de mathématique et de physique, présentés par divers sçavans (Paris)*, Vol. 7 (1776), pp. 343–382.

1.6. W. B. PARSONS: *Engineers and Engineering in the Renaissance*. Williams and Wilkins, Baltimore 1939, p. 72.

1.7. ROBERT HOOKE: *Lectures De Potentia Restitutiva, or of Spring, Explaining the Power of Springing Bodies. To which are added some Collections, viz. A Description of Dr. Pappin's Wind-Fountain and Force-Pump. Mr. Young's Observations concerning Fountains. Some other Considerations concerning that Subject. Captain Sturmy's remarks of a Subterranean Cave and Cistern. Mr. G. T. Observations made on the Pike of Teneriffe, 1674. Some Reflections and Conjectures occasioned thereupon. A Relation of a late Eruption on the Isle of Palma*. S.R.S. London, Printed for John Martyn, Printer to the Royal Society, at the Bell in St. Paul's Church-Yard, 1678.

1.8. R. KIPLING: General Summary. *Departmental Ditties, and other Verses*, Thacker, Sprink and Co., Calcutta 1891, p. 4.

Chapter 2

2.1. GALILEO GALILEI: *Two New Sciences*. Translated by H. Crew and A. de Salvio. Macmillan, New York 1933. p. 115.

2.2. AUGUST FERDINAND MÖBIUS: *Lehrbuch der Statik*. Leipzig 1837. Vol. 2, Chapters 4 and 5.

Chapter 3

3.1. M. BILL: *Robert Maillart*. Editions d'Architecture. Zurich 1951. 180 pp.
3.2. *Second Report of the Steel Structures Research Committee*. H.M. Stationery Office, London 1934. 369 pp.
3.3. R. J. MAINSTONE: *Tests on the New Government Offices, Whitehall Gardens*. National Building Studies, Research Paper No. 28. H.M. Stationery Office, London 1960. 54 pp.
3.4. H. V. HILL: The load bearing capacity of metal structures. *Structural Engineer*, Vol. 33 (1955), pp. 255–263.
3.5. AXEL BENDIXEN: *Die Methode der Alpha Gleichungen zur Berechnung von Rahmenkonstruktionen*. Berlin 1914. (Quoted by S. Timoshenko and D. H. Young, Theory of Structures, McGraw-Hill, New York 1945, p. 362).
3.6. W. M. WILSON AND G. A. MANEY: *Wind stresses in office buildings*. Bulletin No. 80. Engineering Experiment Station, University of Illinois, Urbana 1915.
3.7. A. KLEINLOGEL: *Rigid Frame Formulas*. Frederick Ungar, New York 1952. 460 pp.
3.8. A. KLEINLOGEL AND A. HASELBACH: *Multibay Frames*. Crosby Lockwood, London 1963. 469 pp.
3.9. V. LEONTOVICH: *Frames and Arches*. McGraw-Hill, New York 1959. 472 pp.
3.10. H. J. GREENBERG AND W. PRAGER: Limit design of beams and frames. *Trans. American Society of Civil Engineers*, Vol. 117 (1952), p. 447.
3.11. LYNN S. BEEDLE: *Plastic Design of Steel Frames*. John Wiley, New York 1958. 406 pp.
3.12. G. C. ERNST: Plastic hinging at the intersection of beams and columns. *Jnl. American Concrete Institute*, Vol. 28 (1957), pp. 1119–1144.

Chapter 4

4.1. R. V. SOUTHWELL: *Relaxation Methods in Engineering*, Oxford University Press, London 1940. 252 pp.
4.2. R. K. LIVESLEY: Analysis of rigid frames by an electronic digital computer. *Engineering*, Vol. 176 (1953), pp. 230 and 277.
4.3. Committee on Electronic Computation, Structural Division A.S.C.E.: *Second Conference on Electronic Computation*, Pittsburgh. American Society of Civil Engineers, New York 1960. 673 pp.
4.4. A. S. HALL AND R. W. WOODHEAD: *Frame Analysis—a unified introduction to the matrix analysis of structures*. John Wiley, New York 1961. 247 pp.
4.5. F. L. RYDER: Analogue for forces and moments in a rigid frame. *Proc. American Society of Civil Engineers*, Vol. 79 (1953). Separate No. 376, 24 pp.
4.6. G. E. BEGGS: The accurate mechanical solution of statically indeterminate structures by use of paper models and special gauges. *Jnl. American Concrete Institute*, Vol. 18 (1922), pp. 58–78.

4.7. United States Department of the Interior, Bureau of Reclamation: *Model Tests of the Boulder Dam*. The Bureau, Denver, Colo. 1939. 400 pp.

4.8. E. TORROJA: Rapport sur les voiles minces construits en Espagne. *Final Report of the Third Congress, International Association for Bridge and Structural Engineering*. Liège 1948, pp. 575–584.

4.9. *ISMES—Organization, Plants, Activity*. Bulletin No. 1. Istituto Sperimentale Modelli e Strutture, Bergamo 1953. 22 pp.

4.10. H. J. COWAN: Some applications of the use of direct model analysis in the design of architectural structures. *Jnl. Institution of Engineers, Australia*, Vol. 33 (1961), pp. 259–267.

4.11. F. K. LIGTENBERG: The moiré method, a new experimental method for the determination of moments in small slab models. *Proc. Society for Experimental Stress Analysis*, Vol. 12 (1954), pp. 83–92.

4.12. P. L. NERVI: *Structures*. Dodge, New York 1956. *Chapter 6* Experimental Model Analysis, pp. 87–93.

4.13. R. E. DOHERTY AND G. E. KELLER: *Mathematics in Modern Engineering*, John Wiley, New York 1936. *Vol. I, Chapter 2, Section 5:* Dimensional Analysis, pp. 130–163.

4.14. J. R. NICHOLS: Statical limitations upon the steel requirement in reinforced concrete flat slab floors. *Trans. American Society of Civil Engineers*, Vol. 77 (1914), p. 1670.

4.15. H. M. WESTERGAARD AND W. A. SLATER: Moments and stresses in slabs. *Proc. American Concrete Institute*, Vol. 17 (1921), pp. 415–525.

4.16. D. A. L. SAUNDERS: The reinforced concrete dome of the Melbourne Public Library, 1911. *Architectural Science Review*, Vol. 2 (1959), pp. 39–46.

4.17. G. LAMÉ AND E. CLAPEYRON: Sur l'équilibre intérieur des corps solides homogènes. *Mémoires présentés à l'Académie des Sciences de l'Institute de France*, (Second Series), Vol. 4 (1828), pp. 465–562.

4.18. F. DISCHINGER: *Handbuch für Eisenbeton*, 4th edition, W. Ernst, Berlin 1928. *Schalen und Rippenkuppeln*, Vol. 6, p. 163.
A modern account in English of Dischinger's theory has been given by A. PFLÜGER: *Elementary Statics of Shells*. 2nd edition. F. W. Dodge, New York 1961. 122 pp.

4.19. F. AIMOND: Etude statique des voiles minces en paraboloide hyperbolique travaillant sans flexion. *Publ. International Association for Bridge and Structural Engineering*, Vol. 4 (1936), pp. 1–112.

4.20. W. S. WLASSOW: *Allgemeine Schalentheorie und ihre Anwendung in der Technik*. Akademie Verlag, Berlin 1958. 661 pp. (Translated from the Russian edition of 1949.)

4.21. F. DISCHINGER AND U. FINSTERWALDER: Eisenbeton Schalendächer System Dywidag. *Der Bauingenieur*, Vol. 9 (1928), pp. 807–812, 823–827, and 842–846.

4.22. H. SCHORER: Line load action on thin cylindrical shells. *Trans. American Society of Civil Engineers*, Vol. 101 (1936), pp. 767–810.

4.23. R. S. JENKINS: *Theory and Design of Cylindrical Shell Structures*. Lund und Humphries, London 1947. 75 pp.

4.24. *Design of Cylindrical Shells.* Manual of Engineering Practice No. 31, American Society of Civil Engineers, New York 1952. 175 pp.

4.25. D. RÜDIGER AND J. URBAN: *Circular Cylindrical Shells.* Teubner, Leipzig 1955. 270 pp.

4.26. J. D. BENNETT: Some recent developments in the design of reinforced concrete shell roofs. *Reinforced Concrete Review,* Vol. 5 (1959), pp. 23–62.

4.27. J. E. GIBSON: Automatic programme for multi-shell roofs of general shape. *Architectural Science Review,* Vol. 6 (1963), pp. 2–11.

4.28. G. WINTER AND M. PEI: Hipped plate construction. *Proc. American Concrete Institute,* Vol. 43 (1947), pp. 505-531.

4.29. C. S. WHITNEY: Cantilevered folded plate roofs ACI headquarters. *Proc. American Concrete Institute,* Vol. 55 (1958), pp. 427–430.

4.30. R. W. MARKS: *The Dymaxion World of Buckminster Fuller.* Reinhold, New York 1960. pp. 178–224.

4.31. Z. MAKOWSKI: Braced domes, their history, modern trends and recent developments. *Architectural Science Review,* Vol. 5 (1962), pp. 62–79.

4.32. R. V. SOUTHWELL: Primary stress distribution in space frames. *Engineering,* Vol. 109 (1920), p. 165.

4.33. KONRAD WACHSMANN: *The Turning Point in Building,* Reinhold, New York 1961, pp. 160–193.

4.34. *Hanging Roofs—Proceedings of the IASS Colloquium on Hanging Roofs, Continuous Metallic Shell Roofs and Superficial Lattice Roofs, Paris 1962.* Edited by N. Esquillan and Y. Saillard. North Holland Publishing Co., Amsterdam 1963, pp. 42–208.

4.35. From the Code of Hamurabi, engraved on a column in the Louvre, Paris, dating from approximately 1950 B.C.

Chapter 5

5.1. R. K. MACPHERSON in Chapter 2, "Physiological Background of Air Conditioning". *Air Conditioning,* by N. R. SHERIDAN and others. Queensland University Press, Brisbane 1963, pp. 19–39.

5.2. S. F. MARKHAM: *Climate and the Energy of Nations.* Oxford University Press, London 1947. 240 pp.

5.3. D. BLAGDEN: Experiments and observations in a heated room. *Phil. Trans. Royal Society of London,* Vol. 65 (1775), p. 111.

5.4. T. BEDFORD: *Basic Principles of Ventilation and Heating.* H. K. Lewis, London 1964. *Introduction,* pp. 1–6.

5.5. J. S. HALLDANE: The influence of high air temperature. *Journal of Hygiene (Cambridge),* Vol. 5 (1905), p. 494.

5.6. A. F. DUFTON: *The Equivalent Temperature of a Room and its Measurement.* Building Research Technical Paper No. 13. H.M. Stationery Office, London 1932. 9 pp.

5.7. W. V. MACFARLANE: Thermal comfort zones. *Architectural Science Review,* Vol. 1 (1958), pp. 1–14.

5.8. E. G. A. WEISS: Air conditioning and working efficiency. *Architectural Science Review,* Vol. 2 (1959), pp. 68–76.

5.9. R. N. Morse: The design of air-conditioned buildings. A look into the future—radiant cooling. *Australian Building Science and Technology*, Vol. 4 (1964), No. 11, pp. 36–39.

5.10. R. Leroux: *Ecologie Humaine—Science de l'Habitat*. Editions Eyrolles, Paris 1963. 318 pp.

5.11. L. Thorndike: *The Sphere of Sacrobosco and its Commentators*. University of Chicago Press, 1949, p. 129.

5.12. E. M. Winslow: *A Libation to the Gods—The Story of the Roman Aqueducts*. Hodder and Stoughton, London 1963. 191 pp.

5.13. G. Pleijel: *The computation of natural radiation in architecture and town planning*. Statens Namnd för Byggnadsforskning. Meddelande 25, Stockholm 1954. 143 pp.

5.14. Building Research Station, D.S.I.R.: *Principles of Modern Building*. H.M. Stationery Office, London 1959, Vol. I, pp. 57–71.

5.15. Harrison and Anderson: Illumination efficiencies as determined in an experimental room. *Trans. Illuminating Engineering Society*, Vol. 11 (1916), p. 67.

5.16. J. W. Griffith: *Predicting daylight as interior illumination*. Libbey-Owens-Ford Glass Company, Toledo, Ohio 1958. 27 pp.

5.17. J. E. Flynn and S. M. Mills: *Architectural Lighting Graphics*. Reinhold, New York 1962. *Part 3*. The Influence of Light on Space and Form, pp. 39–56.

5.18. W. C. Sabine: *Selected Papers on Acoustics*. Dover Publications, New York 1964, p. 255.

Chapter 6

6.1. D. B. Harden: Domestic Window Glass—Roman, Saxon, Medieval, in *Studies in Building History*, edited by E. M. Jope. Odhams, London 1961, pp. 39–63.

6.2. J. L. Petersen: History and development of precast concrete in the United States. *Jnl. American Concrete Institute*, Vol. 25 (1954), pp. 477–500.

6.3. Ministry of Works: *House Construction*. Post-War Building Study No. 1. H.M. Stationery Office, London 1944. 152 pp.

6.4. G. H. Ledderboge and others: *Montage von Beton—und Stahlbetonfertigteilen*. V.E.B. Verlag für Bauwesen, Berlin 1964. 410 pp.

6.5. László Mokk: *Prefabricated Concrete for Industrial and Public Structures*. Publishing House of the Hungarian Academy of Science, Budapest 1964. 516 pp.

6.6. V. I. Ovsyankin: The industrialization of house building, with particular reference to the U.S.S.R. *C.I.B. Bulletin*, No. 3 (1962), pp. 10–18.

6.7. *Housing from the Factory*. Cement and Concrete Association, London 1962. 151 pp.

6.8. *System Building 2*. Interbuild, London 1964. 120 pp.

6.9. A. R. Dooley and others: *Casebooks in Production Management*. John Wiley, New York 1964. *Sunshine Builders Inc.*, pp. 164–184.

6.10. C. HOBHOUSE: *1851 and the Crystal Palace*. John Murray, London 1937. 181 pp.

6.11. R. WITTKOWER: *Architectural Principles in the Age of Humanism*. Alec Tiranti, London 1952, pp. 115–116.

6.12. M. CANTOR: *Vorlesungen über die Geschichte der Mathematik*, Leipzig 1900, Vol. II, p. 377.

6.13. LE CORBUSIER: *The Modulor*. Faber and Faber, London 1954. 243 pp.

6.14. E. D. EHRENKRANTZ: *The Modular Number Pattern*. Alec Tiranti, London 1956, 82 pp.

6.15. Directorate General of Research and Development, Ministry of Public Building and Works: The Nenk Method of Building—Dimensional Organization. *Modular Quarterly*, Summer 1963, pp. 10–81.

6.16. C. SIEGEL: *Structure and Form in Modern Architecture*. Crosby Lockwood, London 1962. 308 pp.

6.17. U. CONRADS: *Programme und Manifeste zur Architektur des 20. Jahrhunderts*. Ullstein Verlag, Berlin 1964. 180 pp.

6.18. G. PONTI: *In Praise of Architecture*. F. W. Dodge, New York 1960, p. 45.

6.19. LEWIS CARROLL: *The Hunting of the Snark*. Reprint Society, London 1960, p. 35.

Index